COURSE **2A**

Extra Practice

Authors
Dr. Chee-Chong Lai
May-Kuen Leong
Wai-Cheng Low

Marshall Cavendish
Education

U.S. Distributor

Houghton Mifflin Harcourt

D1065961

© 2018 Marshall Cavendish Education Pte Ltd

Published by Marshall Cavendish Education
Times Centre, 1 New Industrial Road, Singapore 536196
Customer Service Hotline: (65) 6213 9444
US Office Tel: (1-914) 332 8888 | Fax: (1-914) 332 8882
E-mail: tmesales@mceducation.com
Website: www.mceducation.com

Distributed by
Houghton Mifflin Harcourt
222 Berkeley Street
Boston, MA 02116
Tel: 617-351-5000
Website: www.hmheducation.com/mathinfocus

Cover: © Tim Laman/Getty Images

First published 2018

Marshall Cavendish and *Math in Focus*® are registered trademarks of Times Publishing Limited.

Singapore Math® is a trademark of Singapore Math Inc.® and Marshall Cavendish Education Pte Ltd.

ISBN 978-1-328-88020-8

Printed in Singapore

2 3 4 5 6 7 8   1401   23 22 21 20 19 18
4500704403   A B C D E

Contents

CHAPTER

① The Real Number System

Lesson 1.1 Representing Rational Numbers on the Number Line **1**

Lesson 1.2 Writing Rational Numbers as Decimals **3**

Lesson 1.3 Introducing Irrational Numbers **5**

Lesson 1.4 Introducing the Real Number System **7**

Lesson 1.5 Introducing Significant Digits **9**

Brain @ Work **11**

CHAPTER

② Rational Number Operations

Lesson 2.1 Adding Integers **12**

Lesson 2.2 Subtracting Integers **14**

Lesson 2.3 Multiplying and Dividing Integers **16**

Lesson 2.4 Operations with Integers **18**

Lesson 2.5 Operations with Rational Numbers **20**

Lesson 2.6 Operations with Decimals **23**

Brain @ Work **26**

Cumulative Practice for Chapters 1 and 2 ..... **27**

CHAPTER 3

Algebraic Expressions

Lesson 3.1   Adding Algebraic Terms **33**

Lesson 3.2   Subtracting Algebraic Terms **35**

Lesson 3.3   Simplifying Algebraic Expressions **37**

Lesson 3.4   Expanding Algebraic Expressions **40**

Lesson 3.5   Factoring Algebraic Expressions **44**

Lesson 3.6   Writing Algebraic Expressions **46**

Lesson 3.7   Real-World Problems: Algebraic Reasoning **49**

Brain @ Work **51**

CHAPTER 4

Algebraic Equations and Inequalities

Lesson 4.1   Understanding Equivalent Equations **52**

Lesson 4.2   Solving Algebraic Equations **53**

Lesson 4.3   Real-World Problems: Algebraic Equations **56**

Lesson 4.4   Solving Algebraic Inequalities **58**

Lesson 4.5   Real-World Problems: Algebraic Inequalities **60**

Brain @ Work **61**

CHAPTER

 Direct and Inverse Proportion

Lesson 5.1   Understanding Direct Proportion **62**

Lesson 5.2   Representing Direct Proportion Graphically **65**

Lesson 5.3   Solving Direct Proportion Problems **68**

Lesson 5.4   Understanding Inverse Proportion **73**

Brain @ Work **77**

Cumulative Practice for Chapters 3 to 5 .... **78**

Answers **87**

Math in Focus®
Singapore Math®
by Marshall Cavendish

Introducing Math in Focus® Extra Practice

Extra Practice was written to complement **Math in Focus®: Singapore Math® by Marshall Cavendish**. It offers further practice for on-level students and is very similar to the Practice exercises in the Student Books.

Practice to Reinforce and Challenge

Extra Practice provides ample questions to reinforce all concepts taught, and includes challenging questions in the Brain@Work pages. These challenging questions provide extra non-routine problem-solving opportunities, strengthening abstract reasoning powers that include the use of mathematical structures, repeated patterns, models, and tools.

Using the Cumulative Practice

Extra Practice also provides Cumulative Practices that allow students to consolidate learning from several chapters. They can be used to prepare for Benchmark Tests or as another source of good problems for class discussion.

Using the Extra Practice

Extra Practice is an excellent option for homework, or it may be used in class or after school. It is intended for students who simply need more practice to become confident, secure mathematics students who are aiming for excellence.

 Extra Practice is also available online and on the Teacher One Stop.

CHAPTER

The Real Number System

Lesson 1.1   Representing Rational Numbers on the Number Line

Find the absolute value of each fraction. Use a number line to show how far the fraction is from 0. Write fractions in simplest form.

1. $\dfrac{6}{8}$

2. $\dfrac{47}{12}$

3. $-\dfrac{6}{13}$

4. $-\dfrac{36}{15}$

Write each integer or fraction as $\dfrac{m}{n}$ in simplest form where m and n are integers.

5. 12

6. −67

7. $\dfrac{25}{60}$

8. $\dfrac{750}{14}$

Write each mixed number or decimal as $\dfrac{m}{n}$ in simplest form where m and n are integers.

9. $3\dfrac{5}{18}$

10. $-1\dfrac{1}{21}$

11. $12\dfrac{1}{3}$

12. $-72\dfrac{5}{12}$

13. 0.5

14. 2.51

15. 3.495

16. −0.135

17. −1.32

18. −5.52

Name: _____   Date: _____

Complete.

19. Suppose the line below represents a thermometer calibrated in degrees Celsius. Locate each of the following temperatures on the thermometer.

7°C, −2.5°C, −3°C, 3.5°C, −0.8°C

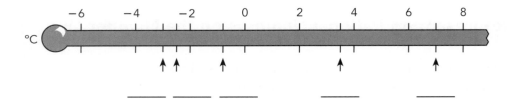

20. Locate the following rational numbers correctly on the number line.

$-40\frac{2}{5}, -\frac{261}{7}, -38\frac{5}{6}$

_____   _____   _____

Graph each rational number on a separate number line.

21. $66\frac{1}{3}$

22. $\frac{135}{6}$

23. $-\frac{11}{12}$

24. $-\frac{79}{11}$

25. 32.4

26. −49.9

Solve.

27. List the numbers below from least to greatest. Then graph them on a number line.

$-4\frac{5}{14}, 6.7, \frac{21}{4}, -3.12, -\frac{22}{7}, 1.01$

Lesson 1.2   Writing Rational Numbers as Decimals

Using long division, write each rational number as a terminating decimal.

1. $\dfrac{7}{16}$

2. $\dfrac{654}{15}$

3. $-\dfrac{9}{24}$

4. $-\dfrac{126}{35}$

Using long division, write each rational number as a repeating decimal with 2 decimal places. Identify the pattern of repeating digits using bar notation.

5. $\dfrac{28}{9}$

6. $8\dfrac{1}{15}$

7. $-56\dfrac{5}{6}$

8. $-\dfrac{2}{11}$

Write each rational number as a repeating decimal using bar notation. You may use a calculator.

9. $\dfrac{5}{11}$

10. $-\dfrac{9}{13}$

11. $-\dfrac{456}{123}$

12. $\dfrac{166}{91}$

 Refer to the list of rational numbers below for questions 13 to 16. You may use a calculator.

$$-2\dfrac{11}{17},\ \dfrac{90}{19},\ \dfrac{63}{10},\ -\dfrac{171}{112},\ 4\dfrac{13}{18}$$

13. Write each rational number as a decimal with at most 4 decimal places.

14. Using your answers in question 13, list the numbers from least to greatest using the symbol $<$.

15. Place each rational number on the same number line.

16. Which rational number is farthest from 0?

Name: _____   Date: _____

Lesson 1.3   Introducing Irrational Numbers

Locate each positive irrational number on the number line using rational approximations. First tell which two whole numbers the square root is between.

1. $\sqrt{8}$

2. $\sqrt{10}$

3. $\sqrt{21}$

4. $\sqrt{37}$

Locate each negative irrational number on the number line using rational approximations. First tell which two integers the square root is between.

5. $-\sqrt{8}$

6. $-\sqrt{14}$

7. $-\sqrt{27}$

8. $-\sqrt{68}$

Use a calculator. Locate each irrational number to 3 decimal places on the number line using rational approximations.

9. $\sqrt{51}$

10. $-\sqrt{279}$

11. $\sqrt[3]{888}$

Locate each irrational number to the nearest hundredth on the number line using rational approximations.

12. $\sqrt{99}$

13. $-\sqrt{1999}$

14. $\sqrt{6655}$

Solve.

15. Locate the value of the constant π^2, on the number line using rational numbers.

16. 1.6175 and $\dfrac{8}{5}$ are two rational approximate values of the golden ratio, φ. φ is given by 1.6180339... ...

a) Graph 1.6175, $\dfrac{8}{5}$, and φ on a number line.

b) Which of the two rational approximate values is closer to φ?

17. The volume of a cube is 130 cubic inches. Write the length of a side of the cube as an irrational number. Approximate the length to 2 decimal places.

Lesson 1.4   Introducing the Real Number System

 Use a calculator. Compare each pair of real numbers using either < or >.

1. $\sqrt{67}$ ☐ $\sqrt{68}$

2. -11.47 ☐ $-\sqrt{149}$

3. 15.489 ☐ $\sqrt{240}$

4. 4.625 ☐ $\dfrac{467}{111}$

Use the irrational numbers below for questions 5 to 7.

$\sqrt{62}$, $\sqrt[3]{999}$, π, $-1.\overline{345}$

5. Find the absolute value of each irrational number to 3 decimal places.

6. Graph each irrational number on a real number line.

7. Order the irrational numbers from greatest to least using the symbol >.

Use the real numbers below for questions 8 and 9.

1.34, $\sqrt{37}$, $-4\dfrac{5}{12}$, $-\dfrac{31}{6}$, $-\sqrt[3]{266}$

8. Complete the table using the real numbers shown.

Rational Numbers	Irrational Numbers

9. Order the real numbers from least to greatest using the symbol <.

Name: _____   Date: _____

Use the real numbers below for questions 10 and 11.

$$\frac{198}{23}, -12.255, -\pi^2, \sqrt{145}, -\sqrt{288}$$

10. 🖩 Represent each real number as a decimal up to 4 decimal places.

11. Locate each number on a real number line.

12. Complete the table using the real numbers shown.

Rational Numbers	Irrational Numbers

Solve.

13. An ice skater is skating at a speed of $\sqrt{\frac{64}{5}}$ miles per second.

    a) About what speed (to 2 decimal places) is the ice skater skating?

    b) If the speed of the skater changes to 4 miles per second, is the skater skating at a speed greater than $\sqrt{\frac{64}{5}}$ miles per second? Explain using a number line.

Lesson 1.5   Introducing Significant Digits

List the significant digits for each number. Then count the number of significant digits.

1. 26,701   _____

2. 70.0311   _____

3. −10.9   _____

4. 0.680   _____

5. 0.00052   _____

6. −0.0007   _____

Round each integer to the given number of significant digits.

7. 4,999 (to 1 significant digit)   _____

8. 46,900 (to 2 significant digits)   _____

9. 6,391,067 (to 3 significant digits)   _____

10. 32,010,067 (to 5 significant digits)   _____

Round each decimal to the given number of significant digits.

11. 0.0871 (to 1 significant digit)   _____

12. −4.602 (to 2 significant digits)   _____

13. −1.995 (to 3 significant digits)   _____

14. −0.0098473 (to 3 significant digits)   _____

15. 2.17098 (to 4 significant digits)   _____

16. 761.1060 (to 5 significant digits)   _____

Solve.

17. Round 8,708,756 to the given number of significant digits.

    a) 1 significant digit   _____

    b) 2 significant digits   _____

    c) 3 significant digits   _____

    d) 4 significant digits   _____

18. Round 46,009.491 to the given number of significant digits.

    a) 4 significant digits   _____

    b) 5 significant digits   _____

    c) 6 significant digits   _____

    d) 7 significant digits   _____

Name: _____   Date: _____

Solve.

19. If a stopwatch is capable of showing a time up to one hundredth of a second, how many significant digits in the reading of 200.0000 seconds are reliable?

20. In Neptune's orbit around the Sun, the farthest point from the Sun is 2,829,691,160 miles. If the distance is rounded to the nearest 100,000, how many of the trailing zeros are significant?

21. A measuring cylinder gives a reading of 3.67 liters. Which significant digit is the least reliable?

22. The current world population is approximately 6,976,950,760. Round this figure to 6 significant digits.

23. The current world record of men's 400-meter dash was completed with a time of 43.18 seconds in 1999. What was the average speed of the runner, in meters per second, correct to 3 significant digits?

24. An engineer wanted to measure the diameter of a metal cylinder. She measured the diameter at different points along the cylinder. Each measurement was rounded to the nearest 0.01 millimeter. She jotted down these measurements: 6, 6.4, 5.75, 5.25, and 5.36.
   a) Given that the measurements were rounded to the nearest 0.01 millimeter, how should she have written the measurements of 6 and 6.4?

   b) Find the mean of the diameters. Give your answer using the correct number of significant digits.

CHAPTER

1. When the decimal place of a certain positive number is moved four places to the right, the new number is 9 times the reciprocal of the original number. What is the original number?

2. How many positive integers are there for a such that $\dfrac{a}{3}$ and $2a$ are both three-digit integers?

CHAPTER

Rational Number Operations

Lesson 2.1   Adding Integers

Evaluate each sum using a number line.

1. $-7 + 9$

2. $4 + (-7)$

3. $8 + (-8)$

4. $-2 + (-5)$

5. $5 + (-8)$

6. $-10 + 10$

Evaluate each sum using absolute values.

7. $18 + (-39)$

8. $62 + (-18)$

9. $-25 + 14$

10. $-43 + 72$

11. $-19 + (-32)$

12. $-57 + (-21)$

Evaluate each sum.

13. $-7 + 12 + 9$

14. $-88 + 35 + 27$

15. $14 + (-20) + (-6)$

16. $-31 + (-5) + 12$

17. $-45 + (-27) + (-41)$

18. $16 + (-54) + 23$

Name: _____   Date: _____

Solve. Show your work.

19. A submarine was cruising at a depth of 340 feet below sea level. Find the depth of the submarine after it ascends 76 feet.

20. The boiling point of nitrogen gas is −320°F and the boiling point of oxygen gas is 23°F greater than that of nitrogen. What is the boiling point of oxygen gas?

21. Daryl played a game that has four stages. The final score is the sum of the scores at each stage. Daryl scored 50, −85, −12, and 93 points at each of the four stages. Find Daryl's final score.

22. Jack bought a stock for $26 a share. The daily changes in the stock price for the next four days were −5, −2, +1, and −6. How much was the stock worth at the end of the four days?

23. The temperature recorded at 6 A.M. was −3°F. Six hours later the temperature had increased by 18°F. Find the temperature at noon.

Lesson 2.2   Subtracting Integers

Evaluate each expression.

1. 9 − 11

2. 46 − 87

3. 30 − 40

4. 28 − (−15)

5. −14 − (−12)

6. −113 − (−58)

7. −5 − 17 − 23

8. −3 − (−6) − 10

9. −8 − (−12) − 31

10. −47 − (−20) − (−67)

11. −93 − (−17) − (−53)

12. −16 − (−9) − (−16)

Find the distance between each pair of integers.

13. 8 and 32

14. 15 and 64

15. −27 and 18

16. −9 and 35

17. −24 and −11

18. −35 and −7

Solve. Show your work.

19. At 2 A.M., the temperature was −6°C. An hour later, the temperature had decreased by 8°C. What is the new temperature?

20. A diver was swimming at a depth of 28 feet below sea level. He then dove 35 feet further. What is his new depth relative to sea level?

Name: _____   Date: _____

21. In the United States, the largest recorded temperature change over a 24-hour period occurred on January 15, 1972 in Loma, Montana. The temperature increased from −54°F to 49°F. Find the temperature difference.

22. The highest elevation of the continent of North America is at Mt. McKinley, at 20,320 feet above sea level. The lowest elevation is at Death Valley, at 282 feet below sea level. What is the difference in the elevations of these two locations?

23. The highest temperature ever recorded on Earth was 134°F at Death Valley, California in 1913. The lowest temperature ever recorded was −129°F at Vostok Station, Antarctica in 1983. Calculate the difference between these temperatures.

24. The record low temperature in Oklahoma was −31°F. The record low temperature in South Dakota is 27°F lower than −31°F. What is the record low in South Dakota?

25. Steve and Simon participated in a gaming competition. Steve's final score was 480 points. Simon's final score was 570 points less than Steve's final score. What was Simon's final score?

Lesson 2.3   Multiplying and Dividing Integers

Evaluate each product.

1. $7 \cdot (-9)$

2. $12 \cdot (-8)$

3. $-3 \cdot 11$

4. $-5 \cdot 6$

5. $-6 \cdot (-8)$

6. $-7 \cdot (-15)$

7. $-30 \cdot (0)$

8. $0 \cdot (-19)$

9. $4 \cdot (-6) \cdot (10)$

10. $7 \cdot 8 \cdot (-9)$

11. $-11(5)(-4)$

12. $-2(-21)(3)$

13. $6(-14)(-17)$

14. $-4(-28)(-9)$

15. $-3(-12)(-10)$

16. $-8(0)(-27)$

17. $-50(-6)(0)$

18. $-9(-8)(2)(3)$

19. $-5(7)(-4)(-5)$

20. $-10(-3)(-6)(-2)$

Name: _____   Date: _____

Evaluate each quotient.

21. $357 \div (-7)$

22. $560 \div (-16)$

23. $-720 \div 12$

24. $-550 \div 11$

25. $-189 \div (-9)$

26. $-112 \div (-4)$

27. $0 \div (-20)$

28. $0 \div (-5)$

Solve. Show your work.

29. A hot air balloon descended 2,250 feet in 15 minutes. Find the change in altitude per minute.

30. A diver descends at a rate of 2 feet per minute. How far is he below sea level after 40 minutes?

31. Over 3 months, the average change in a company's sales income was $9 million. Determine the average change in sales income per month.

32. A share of stock decreased $2 in value each day for 7 days. Find the total change in the stock's value.

Lesson 2.4 Operations with Integers

Evaluate each expression.

1. $-5 \cdot 8 + 12$

2. $20 - 4 \cdot (-6)$

3. $3 \cdot (-9) + (-2) \cdot (7)$

4. $150 \div (-5) + (-38)$

5. $-48 \div 4 \cdot (-5) - 17$

6. $-35 - 490 \div 7 + 12$

7. $82 - (9 - 13) \cdot 9$

8. $-27 - (4 + 4) \cdot 3$

9. $90 \div (-6 - 3) + 45$

10. $(16 + 2)(3) - 5(-5 + 3)$

11. $-30 + 5(3 + 8) - 45$

12. $25 \div [-4 + (-1)] - 9(3)$

13. $36 \div 6 - (-25 + 15)(4)$

14. $-42 + 70 \div (-2 - 3) + 84 \div (4 + 2)$

15. $-200 + 32(-3 + 7) - 45(15 - 20)$

16. $480 \div (6 + 14) - 7(4) + 8(3 + 4)$

Solve. Show your work.

17. Cecilia has an 8-inch by 12-inch sheet of rectangular paper. She cuts out identical 4-inch by 3-inch rectangles from two corners of the paper. She then cuts out identical right triangles from the other two corners of the paper. Using the diagram shown, find the area of the remaining paper.

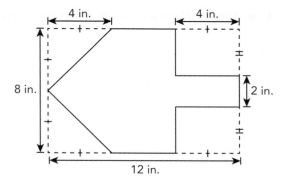

18. Today, a tank contains 6,600 gallons of water. For the past 3 days, 210 gallons of water was pumped out of the tank each day. What was the volume of water in the tank 3 days ago?

Name: _____   Date: _____

Lesson 2.5   Operations with Rational Numbers

Evaluate each expression. Give your answer in simplest form.

1. $-\dfrac{8}{3} + \dfrac{1}{4}$

2. $\dfrac{4}{15} + \left(-\dfrac{7}{9}\right)$

3. $-\dfrac{7}{15} + \dfrac{4}{5}$

4. $\dfrac{-5}{8} + \left(-\dfrac{1}{3}\right)$

5. $\dfrac{2}{3} - \left(-\dfrac{5}{9}\right)$

6. $\dfrac{1}{6} - \left(\dfrac{-2}{3}\right)$

7. $-\dfrac{1}{5} - \dfrac{2}{15}$

8. $\dfrac{-1}{7} - \dfrac{3}{14}$

9. $\dfrac{-3}{4} - \left(-\dfrac{1}{2}\right)$

10. $-\dfrac{2}{5} - \left(\dfrac{-3}{4}\right) - \dfrac{5}{8}$

11. $\dfrac{1}{3} - \left(-\dfrac{2}{5}\right) - \dfrac{3}{4}$

12. $\dfrac{-2}{9} - \left(\dfrac{-1}{3}\right) - \left(\dfrac{-3}{5}\right)$

13. $-\dfrac{5}{6} + \left(\dfrac{-3}{4}\right) + \dfrac{5}{8}$

14. $\dfrac{-4}{9} + \left(\dfrac{-5}{6}\right) + \left(\dfrac{-1}{3}\right)$

Evaluate each product. Give your answer in simplest form.

15. $-\dfrac{3}{4} \cdot \dfrac{5}{12}$

16. $-2\dfrac{1}{4} \cdot \dfrac{8}{27}$

17. $-\dfrac{14}{25} \cdot \left(-1\dfrac{3}{7}\right)$

18. $1\dfrac{8}{27} \cdot \left(-2\dfrac{2}{5}\right)$

19. $-2\dfrac{2}{3} \cdot \left(-3\dfrac{3}{4}\right)$

20. $\dfrac{2}{15} \cdot \left(-1\dfrac{2}{3}\right)$

Evaluate each quotient. Give your answer in simplest form.

21. $-\dfrac{1}{4} \div \dfrac{3}{8}$

22. $\dfrac{2}{5} \div \left(-\dfrac{4}{35}\right)$

23. $-\dfrac{1}{6} \div \left(-\dfrac{5}{18}\right)$

24. $1\dfrac{2}{3} \div \left(-3\dfrac{1}{3}\right)$

25. $-2\dfrac{3}{4} \div \left(-1\dfrac{3}{8}\right)$

26. $\dfrac{-10}{\left(\dfrac{5}{13}\right)}$

27. $\dfrac{\left(\dfrac{2}{3}\right)}{-16}$

28. $\dfrac{\left(\dfrac{7}{8}\right)}{\left(-\dfrac{3}{4}\right)}$

29. $\dfrac{\left(-\dfrac{4}{5}\right)}{\left(-\dfrac{7}{20}\right)}$

30. $\dfrac{\left(-2\dfrac{2}{5}\right)}{\left(1\dfrac{1}{5}\right)}$

Solve. Show your work.

31. A restaurant used $8\frac{5}{6}$ pounds of rice on Monday and $5\frac{1}{6}$ pounds of rice on Tuesday. How many more pounds of rice was used on Monday than on Tuesday?

32. Janet has $9\frac{2}{3}$ feet of cloth. She needs to cut it into lengths of $\frac{1}{3}$ feet. How many complete lengths can she cut?

33. A recipe calls for $2\frac{1}{2}$ cups of walnuts. Only $\frac{5}{6}$ cup of walnuts are on hand. How many more cups of walnuts does a chef need for the recipe?

34. The sum of two rational numbers is $-8\frac{1}{4}$. If one of the numbers is $-5\frac{2}{3}$, find the other number.

35. Parcel P weighs $4\frac{1}{2}$ pounds, Parcel Q weighs $3\frac{2}{5}$ pounds and Parcel R weighs $6\frac{4}{5}$ pounds. Find the average weight of the three parcels.

Lesson 2.6   Operations with Decimals

Evaluate each sum or difference.

1. $-3.15 + 7.9$

2. $0.072 + (-5.3)$

3. $-41.36 + (-8.2)$

4. $8.22 - (-0.355)$

5. $-17.203 - 0.86$

6. $-29.5 - (-9.34)$

Evaluate each product.

7. $0.4 \cdot (-5.7)$

8. $-2.7 \cdot 3.1$

9. $-4.36 \cdot (-1.8)$

10. $3.04 \cdot (-6.3)$

Evaluate each quotient.

11. $-36.9 \div 4.5$

12. $159.12 \div (-3.4)$

13. $-49.14 \div (-6.3)$

14. $12.376 \div 0.52$

Evaluate each expression.

15. $-0.48 + (-0.1) + (-2.3)$

16. $-3.59 + 16.7 + (-150.06)$

17. $49.03 + (-7.8) - (-21.05)$

18. $601.03 - 467.9 + (-8.12)$

19. $21.4 - 6.2 + 4.2 \cdot 0.3 - 2.6$

20. $(39.3 + 6) \div 3 + 0.8 \cdot 4$

Name: _____   Date: _____

Solve. Show your work.

21. On Sunday, the balance in Christina's savings account was $315.12. On Monday, she makes withdrawals of $78.95 and $143.80. On Tuesday, she deposits $63.79. What is her balance after she makes the deposit?

22. The table shows the activity in George's savings account.

Date	Deposit	Withdrawal	Balance
January 31	–	–	$148.20
February 5	$35.65	$182.30	$1.55
February 18	$120.83	$78.32	?

What is the balance in George's account on February 18?

23. The highest temperature recorded was 118.4°F in Athens in 1977. The lowest temperature recorded in Ust Shchugor was 191°F lower than that of the highest temperature recorded. What is the lowest temperature recorded?

24. In 2010, a company reported a net income loss of $23,800,000. In 2011, the company reported a net income gain of $10,400,000. How much more did the company earn in 2011 than in 2010?

25. Fiona has only $10 to pay the fees for three art projects. The fees of the projects are $2.50, $6.75, and $2.80. How much more money does she need?

26. In Fairbanks, Alaska, the average temperature in January is −9.7°F. The average temperature in July is 62.4°F. On average, how many degrees colder is Fairbanks in January than in July?

27. A buyer purchased 6 baseball hats for $76.50. The hats will be sold in his retail store for a profit. If he plans to price each hat to make a 40% profit, what should be the selling price of each hat?

28. What is the discount price of a skateboard that costs $155.80 if it is on sale for 20% off?

29. The table shows the temperatures for the first 5 days of January in Lansing, Michigan. Find the average temperature for these 5 days.

January	1	2	3	4	5
Temperature (°C)	−5.2	−6.7	−9.1	−10.3	−8.6

30. Wendy has $50. She wants to buy a book that costs $26.50 and a bag that costs $19.50. The sales tax in her state is 6%. Does Wendy have enough money to buy the book and the bag? If so, how much money does she have left? If not, how much more money does she need?

CHAPTER

2 Brain @ Work

1. If you start with an integer, and subtract −85, add −57, subtract 68, add −77, add 55, and subtract −73, the result is 0. Find the integer that you start with.

2. For each of the following equations, insert brackets so that the each equation is a true statement.

   a)   −20 + 4 · 2 + 7 − 35 = −19

   b)   −15 − 30 ÷ 10 − 15 = −9

   c)   −(−5) + 4 · 2 − 7 = −45

   d)   9 − 15 · 2 − 4 = 12

3. A multiplication magic square is a square in which the product of the numbers in each horizontal, vertical, and diagonal line is a constant. Complete the magic square by finding the missing numbers.

−24	36	2
1		144
	4	

Cumulative Practice
for Chapters 1 and 2

Using long division, write each rational number as a terminating or a repeating decimal. Identify a pattern of repeating digits using bar notation.

1. $\dfrac{13}{4}$

2. $-\dfrac{5}{11}$

3. $-\dfrac{72}{150}$

4. $3\dfrac{11}{12}$

Write each decimal as $\dfrac{m}{n}$ in simplest form where m and n are integers with $n \neq 0$.

5. 2.65

6. −7.4

7. 48.17

8. −0.225

Write each irrational number as a rational approximation correct to 2 decimal places.

9. $\sqrt{13}$

10. $-\sqrt{980}$

11. $-\sqrt[3]{3,401}$

12. $\dfrac{\pi^2}{5}$

Name: _____   Date: _____

Locate each irrational number to the nearest hundredth on the number line using rational approximations.

13. $\sqrt{45}$

14. $-\sqrt{12}$

15. $\sqrt[3]{-769}$

16. Order the following real numbers from least to greatest using the symbol $<$.

$-34.2, \sqrt{79}, -\dfrac{156}{15}, 8.6\overline{57}, -\pi^3$

Complete.

17. Round 45,908 correct to 2 significant digits.

18. Evaluate $\sqrt{63}$ correct to 3 significant digits.

Evaluate each expression.

19. $12 - (-4)$

20. $25 - (-16)$

21. $8 + (-10)$

22. $-11 + (-28)$

23. $3 + (-8) + 7$

24. $-6 + 8 - 5$

25. $-5 - 3 - (-4)$

26. $-350 + 420$

27. $-108 - (-113)$

28. $33 + (-85) - (-12)$

Evaluate each product or quotient. As needed, give your answer in simplest form.

29. $-14 \cdot 6$

30. $-99 \div (-9)$

31. $\dfrac{5}{16} \cdot \left(-\dfrac{8}{15}\right)$

32. $-\dfrac{3}{8} \div \left(-\dfrac{27}{6}\right)$

33. $1\dfrac{5}{11} \cdot \left(-2\dfrac{1}{5}\right)$

34. $\dfrac{\left(-\dfrac{2}{3}\right)}{\left(3\dfrac{1}{6}\right)}$

Evaluate each expression.

35. $-4[10 - (-7)] + [(-9) + 3(-4)] \div 7$

36. $\frac{3}{5}\left(\frac{1}{3} - \frac{5}{6}\right) + 1\frac{4}{15} + 2\left(-\frac{9}{20}\right)$

37. $-3[4.1 - (-2.3)] - 0.4[-6.7 + 3(2.4)]$

38. $-\frac{1}{4}[-18 + 2.4(-3.5 + 2.5)] + 2\frac{1}{4} + (-8.4)$

39. $\dfrac{-\frac{5}{6} + 1\frac{1}{3}}{3\left[\frac{1}{6} - \left(-\frac{4}{9}\right)\right]}$

Name: _____   Date: _____

Solve. Show your work.

40. The circumference of a circle is 83.5 centimeters. Calculate the radius of the circle correct to 3 significant digits. Use 3.14 as an approximation for π.

41. The speed of 4 racing cars are 146.633 miles per hour, 150 miles per hour, 151.971 miles per hour, and 141.428 miles per hour. Find the average speed of the 4 cars correct to 5 significant digits.

42. A diver was swimming 62 feet below sea level. He then dove 39 feet further down. He ascended 48 feet after a while. Find the new depth of the diver.

43. A football team gained 15 yards on a first down, lost 12 yards on the second down, and lost another 6 yards on the third down. How many yards does the team need to gain on the fourth down to have a 10 yard gain from their starting position?

44. Find the difference in height between the top of a 864-feet hill and shifting rock 68 feet below sea level.

45. A 30 question survey gives the following points for responses A, B, C, and D: A = 5, B = 3, C = −2, and D = −4. A person's score is found by totaling the points for all responses. Jason gave 8 A responses, 6 B responses, 12 C responses, and 4 D responses. Find Jason's score for the survey.

46. The highest temperature ever recorded in Bolivia was 116.1°F in Villamontes, Tarija Department. The lowest temperature ever recorded was −14.3°F in Uyuni, Potosi Department. Find the range of temperatures in Bolivia.

47. Two wooden planks have a length of $4\frac{1}{4}$ feet and $2\frac{1}{2}$ feet. A new plank is created by overlapping the ends of the two planks using diagonal cuts and fastening them together. If the length of the overlap is 5 inches long, what is the length, in feet, of the new plank?

48. A hot air balloon was flying at an altitude of 2,150 feet. It took the balloon 4 minutes to descend to 1,430 feet. Find the average change in balloon height.

CHAPTER

Algebraic Expressions

Lesson 3.1   Adding Algebraic Terms

Simplify each expression with decimal coefficients.

1. $0.8x + 0.5x$

2. $0.1y + 0.9y$

3. $1.4p + 0.3p$

4. $0.8m + 2.7m$

5. $2.3a + 0.8a$

6. $1.1b + 2.8b$

Simplify each expression with fractional coefficients.

7. $\frac{1}{7}p + \frac{5}{7}p$

8. $\frac{3}{5}a + \frac{2}{5}a$

9. $\frac{4}{9}m + \frac{2}{9}m$

10. $\frac{5}{8}b + \frac{1}{8}b$

Simplify each expression with fractional coefficients by rewriting the fractions.

11. $\frac{4}{7}x + \frac{5}{14}x$

12. $\frac{2}{5}y + \frac{3}{10}y$

13. $\frac{3}{8}p + \frac{3}{16}p$

14. $\frac{2}{9}m + \frac{2}{3}m$

15. $\frac{2}{3}x + \frac{1}{4}x$

16. $\frac{5}{12}y + \frac{3}{4}y$

Name: _____   Date: _____

Solve. Show your work.

17. The figure shows triangles A and B. Write and simplify an algebraic expression for each of the following.
    a) The perimeter of triangle A
    b) The perimeter of triangle B
    c) The sum of the perimeters of the two triangles

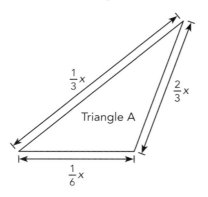
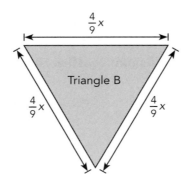

18. The length and width of two rectangular greeting cards are shown. Find the sum of the areas of the two cards.

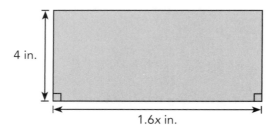
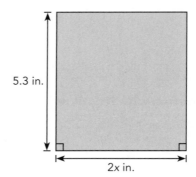

Lesson 3.2   Subtracting Algebraic Terms

Simplify each expression with decimal coefficients.

1. $1.7x - 0.5x$

2. $1.9y - 1.6y$

3. $2.4p - 1.8p$

4. $3.8q - 2.5q$

5. $3.2a - 2.9a$

6. $1.3b - 0.9b$

Simplify each expression with fractional coefficients.

7. $\dfrac{7}{9}x - \dfrac{4}{9}x$

8. $\dfrac{6}{7}y - \dfrac{2}{7}y$

9. $\dfrac{9}{10}p - \dfrac{7}{10}p$

10. $\dfrac{5}{8}m - \dfrac{3}{8}m$

Simplify each expression with fractional coefficients by rewriting the fractions.

11. $\dfrac{4}{5}y - \dfrac{1}{3}y$

12. $\dfrac{5}{6}x - \dfrac{4}{5}x$

13. $\dfrac{7}{9}p - \dfrac{1}{3}p$

14. $\dfrac{10}{3}m - \dfrac{7}{4}m$

15. $\dfrac{9}{7}a - \dfrac{1}{3}a$

16. $\dfrac{7}{10}b - \dfrac{2}{5}b$

Name: _____   Date: _____

Solve. Show your work.

17. The length of Rope A and Rope B are shown. Find the difference in the length of the two ropes.

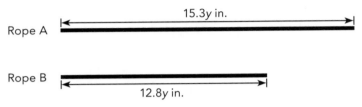

Rope A

Rope B

18. The length and width of a rectangular photo frame with a shaded border are shown. Find the area of the shaded border.

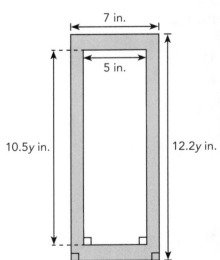

Lesson 3.3   Simplifying Algebraic Expressions

Simplify each expression.

1. $2.1x + 0.8x - 3$

2. $1.6y + 1.9y + 1.3$

3. $3.5p - 2.8p - 1$

4. $4.2q - 3.7q - 5$

5. $\dfrac{5}{9}a + \dfrac{4}{9}a + \dfrac{5}{9}$

6. $\dfrac{7}{8}b + \dfrac{1}{4}b - 3$

7. $\dfrac{9}{2}m - \dfrac{1}{3}m + 7$

8. $\dfrac{8}{3}n - \dfrac{8}{9}n - 3$

Simplify each expression with three algebraic terms.

9. $1.5x + 0.8x + 0.6x$

10. $3.2y + 4.7y + 0.6y$

11. $5.4a - 2.7a - 0.8a$

12. $4.8b + 1.2b - 3.9b$

13. $\dfrac{1}{7}p + \dfrac{4}{7}p + \dfrac{1}{7}p$

14. $\dfrac{7}{9}q + \dfrac{1}{3}q + \dfrac{1}{9}q$

15. $\dfrac{3}{4}m + \dfrac{2}{3}m - \dfrac{1}{6}m$

16. $\dfrac{7}{8}n + \dfrac{3}{4}n - \dfrac{1}{2}n$

Simplify each expression.

17. $4x + 9 + 8x$

18. $5y + 3 + 11y$

19. $7a - 5 - 3a$

20. $16b - 9 + 5b$

21. $1.1p + 2.3 - 0.5p$

22. $6.3q - 1.8 - 5.7q$

23. $\frac{3}{5}m + \frac{2}{3} + \frac{7}{10}m$

24. $\frac{5}{6}n - \frac{2}{3} - \frac{1}{2}n$

Simplify each expression with two variables.

25. $5x + x + 5y$

26. $13x + 9x + 4y$

27. $15p - 8p + 6q$

28. $24m - 16m + 5n$

29. $11a + 3a + 5b - b$

30. $9b - 2a + 3b - a$

31. $2.7m + 0.5m + 3.2n + 0.8n$

32. $18.5p - 16.6p - 4.3q + 2.7q$

33. $\frac{3}{7}x + \frac{1}{7}x - \frac{1}{6}y + \frac{5}{6}y$

34. $\frac{3}{4}p - \frac{1}{2}p + \frac{5}{9}q - \frac{1}{3}q$

35. $6.4m + 2.3n - 5.7m - 0.7n$

36. $6.9a - 4.9b - 7.8a - 0.4b$

37. $\frac{8}{9}x - \frac{4}{5}y - \frac{2}{3}x - \frac{1}{2}y$

38. $\frac{8}{5}a - \frac{7}{4}b - \frac{2}{3}a + \frac{5}{8}b$

Find the perimeter of each figure.

39.

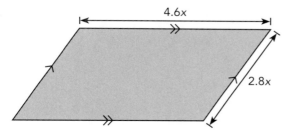

40.

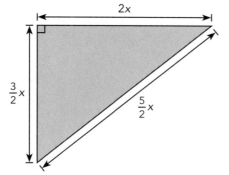

Lesson 3.4 Expanding Algebraic Expressions

Expand each expression.

1. $\frac{1}{4}(8x + 16)$

2. $\frac{1}{3}(3p + 12)$

3. $\frac{1}{2}(14k - 10)$

4. $\frac{1}{8}(8a - 24)$

5. $\frac{1}{2}(4p + 1)$

6. $\frac{1}{7}(2a + 5)$

7. $\frac{1}{5}(3b - 2)$

8. $\frac{3}{5}(2k - 15)$

9. $2(6x + 0.1)$

10. $5(0.3y + 2)$

11. $0.3(5x + 3)$

12. $0.4(2h + 7)$

13. $0.6(m - 4)$

14. $0.5(p - 3)$

15. $0.2(1.2d + 0.3)$

16. $1.5(0.4x - 1.3)$

Expand each expression with a negative factor.

17. $-3(x + 2)$

18. $-5(2x + 3)$

19. $-2(3a + 7b)$

20. $-7(4k - h)$

21. $-6\left(\dfrac{1}{2}p + 3\right)$

22. $-\dfrac{1}{4}\left(8x - \dfrac{1}{3}\right)$

23. $-3(4k + 1.2)$

24. $-4(0.3m + 7)$

25. $-5(q - 0.6)$

26. $-0.2(0.6y - 2)$

Expand and simplify each expression.

27. $2(3y + 2) + 5$

28. $4(3a + 1) - 2$

29. $3(x + 8) + 5x$

30. $7(b + 4) - 3b$

31. $3\left(\dfrac{1}{4}a + 2\right) + 5$

32. $6\left(\dfrac{1}{12}a - 3\right) - \dfrac{1}{2}a$

33. $0.4(x + 3) + 0.8x$

34. $0.3(y + 5) - 0.1y$

35. $-3(5m + 1) - m$

36. $12 - 4(n - 2)$

37. $-0.6(r + 4) + 2.5r$

38. $-(1.4x + 5) + 1.7x$

Expand and simplify each expression with two variables.

39. $15y + 4(8y + x)$

40. $9a + 7(2a - b)$

41. $6g + 8(v - g)$

42. $12p + 10(p - 2q)$

43. $7(2a + b) + 2(3a + b)$

44. $4(2m - n) + 8(3n - m)$

45. $5(3d + e) - 4(d - 4e)$

46. $6(4q - p) - (2q - 5p)$

47. $-3(x + 2y) + 4(3x - 6y)$

48. $-8(y + 3t) - 4(2y - t)$

Name: _____   Date: _____

Write an expression for the missing dimension of each shaded figure and a multiplication expression for its area. Then expand and simplify the multiplication expression.

49.

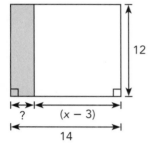

50.

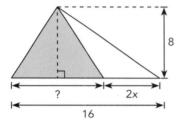

Write an expression for the area of the figure. Expand and simplify.

51.

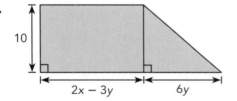

Lesson 3.5   Factoring Algebraic Expressions

Factor each expression with two terms.

1. $3x + 15$

2. $8a + 8$

3. $4x - 28$

4. $5x - 15$

5. $6a + 6b$

6. $2x + 10y$

7. $21p + 7q$

8. $16w + 80m$

9. $3j - 18k$

10. $12t - 48u$

11. $25a - 5p$

12. $8h - 56f$

13. $16x - 10y$

14. $24a - 6b$

15. $35c - 15d$

16. $14y - 30e$

17. $-3 - p$

18. $-y - 8$

19. $-4d - 5$

20. $-5y - 16$

Factor each expression with negative terms.

21. $-2a - 4$

22. $-3x - 24$

23. $-7k - 35$

24. $-9u - 81$

25. $-2 - 6n$

26. $-4 - 12p$

27. $-24x - 18y$

28. $-35m - 20n$

29. $-28w - 7q$

30. $-48y - 16x$

Factor each expression with three terms.

31. $3x + 3y + 9$

32. $4a + 2b + 6$

33. $15p + 5q + 10$

34. $18d + 9e + 12$

35. $4s - 8t - 20$

36. $7a - 14b - 28$

37. $16a - 12b - 6$

38. $33g - 11h - 66$

39. $9 + 18m - 12n$

40. $35 - 5w + 25k$

Name: _____ Date: _____

Lesson 3.6 Writing Algebraic Expressions

Translate each verbal description into an algebraic expression. Simplify the expression when you can.

1. Sum of one-half t and one-third s

2. Twenty subtracted from $\frac{15}{23}b$

3. Product of $5r$ and 7 divided by 15

4. 120% of the sum of w and one-twelfth u

5. Nine-fourteenths of $6x$ reduced by 10

6. 20% of one-half w

7. Seven-tenths of the product of $5p$ and 3

8. Sum of x, three-fourths x, and 90% of z

9. Four times the difference of one-half x subtracted from three-eighths y

10. 60% of the difference of five-eighteenths v subtracted from four-sixths w

46   **Chapter 3** Lesson 3.6

Solve. You may use a diagram, model, or table.

11. The length of a picture frame is $(8u - 12)$ inches. Its width is $\frac{3}{4}$ of its length. Express the width of the picture frame in terms of u.

12. If 6 tablespoons are equivalent to 1 fluid ounce, how many fluid ounces are in $(10t - 4)$ tablespoons?

13. 11 notebooks were added to w notebooks. 7 friends then shared the notebooks equally. Express the number of notebooks each person received in terms of w.

14. A pear costs $0.40 and an apple costs $0.25. What is the total cost of p pears and q apples?

15. The ratio of the number of pencils to pens is 5 : 7. There are q pens. Express the number of pencils in terms of q.

16. When 5 adults joined a group of *y* diners, the ratio of the number of adults to children in the restaurant became 3 : 5. Express the number of children in terms of *y*.

17. Freddy paid *w* dollars for a camera and $120 for an additional camera lens. If the sales tax is 8%, how much did Freddy pay for the camera and lens, including the sales tax?

18. Emily has 5*u* game cards. John has $\frac{8}{13}$ fewer game cards than Emily. Find the average number of game cards that Emily and John have in all in terms of *u*.

19. A train traveled at 140 miles per hour for $2\frac{1}{14}x$ hours, and (2*x* − 3) miles per hour for the next 3 hours.
   a) Express the total distance traveled by the train in terms of *x*.

   b) If *x* = 3, what is the total distance traveled by the train?

Lesson 3.7   Real-World Problems: Algebraic Reasoning

Solve each question using algebraic reasoning.

1. Jeremy has two ropes. The longer rope is $(12.5x + 17)$ centimeters long, and the shorter rope is $(5x + 0.4w)$ centimeters long. Find the difference in length of the two ropes.

2. The radius of a circle is $(7n - 21)$ inches. Find the circumference of the circle in terms of n. Use $\frac{22}{7}$ as an approximation for π.

3. The average daily sales at a bookstore was $(7.6k + 2.2)$ dollars over a 4-day promotion. Find the total sales during the promotion.

4. The ratio of the number of red ribbons to yellow ribbons is 17 to 6. If the number of red ribbons is $2m + 5$, how many ribbons are yellow?

5. During summer vacation, 36% of c children went to Europe, 24 children to Asia, and the rest of the children went to South America. How many children went to South America?

Name: _____ Date: _____

6. The hourly rates for a parking garage are as follows:

First hour	$4.00
Each additional hour thereafter	$3.20

Robyn parked her car in the garage for y hours. How much was her parking fee?

7. A cylinder contains $(4.5x + 2y - 6)$ milliliters of liquid. How many milliliters of liquid must be added to the cylinder to make a total of $(6.9x - 3y + 3)$ milliliters?

8. Among the 50 children at a book fair, b of them are boys. 30% of the girls at the book fair are younger than twelve years old while 40% of the boys are at least twelve years old. How many children at the book fair are younger than twelve years old?

9. When $\frac{2}{5}$ of the koi was given away, there were still b koi and k goldfish left in the pond. How many koi and goldfish were there initially?

10. The ratio of the mass of Bottle A to Bottle B to Bottle C is 7 : 5 : 11. The total mass of Bottle A and Bottle C is $(2x - 9)$ kilograms.
a) Express the mass of Bottle B in terms of x.

b) If $x = 15$, find the mass of Bottle B.

CHAPTER

 3 **Brain @ Work**

Solve. Show your work.

1. Bradley is thinking of three numbers. The first number is 3 less than $\frac{8}{5}$ of the second number, and the second number is $\frac{5}{16}$ of the third number. If the third number is $\frac{2}{3}x - 12$, express the first number in terms of x.

2. $\frac{3}{7}$ of Jar A is filled with water. The capacity of Jar B is p pints. When all the water from Jar A is poured into Jar B, it only fills 8 pints more than 30% of Jar B. When the water is poured into Jar C, it fills 5 pints less than half the capacity of Jar C.
    a) What is the capacity of Jar A in terms of p?

    b) What is the capacity of Jar C in terms of p?

CHAPTER

 4 # Algebraic Equations and Inequalities

Lesson 4.1   Understanding Equivalent Equations

Tell whether each pair of equations are equivalent. Give a reason for your answer.

1. $4x + 1 = 9$ and $2x + 1 = 5$

2. $y + 5 = 7$ and $5y = 10$

3. $5z - 3 = 4$ and $z = -1$

4. $3p - 4 = 8$ and $2p = 4$

5. $7m + 6 - 5 = 15$ and $2m + 5 = 9$

6. $7x + 3 = -4$ and $5x = -5$

7. $3x - 5 + 3x = 7$ and $3x + 1 = 7$

8. $2x - 3 = 0$ and $x + 3 = 0$

9. $\frac{2}{5}x - 3 = 1$ and $\frac{3}{4}x = \frac{15}{2}$

10. $-3x + 4 = 1$ and $x = -1$

Match each equation with an equivalent equation.

11. $8x = 16$

a) $x = 1$

12. $x + 3 = 6$

b) $x = 2$

13. $2x + 13 = 9$

c) $2x = 6$

14. $4 - 5x = -1$

d) $3x - 4 = 14$

15. $\frac{1}{3}x - 2 = 0$

e) $1 + x = -1$

6. Mr. Sidney rented a car for a day. The rental fee consists of a flat rate of $19.99 plus $0.21 per additional mile. For how many miles did Mr. Sidney drive the car if he paid $52.54 for the car rental?

7. A food manufacturer donates money to schools based on the number of its product labels the school collects. The students at one school collected 2,100 product labels in three months. The number of labels collected in the first two months was three times the number of labels collected in the third month. How many product labels were collected in the third month?

8. Find the length of the sides of triangle *ABC* if its perimeter is 33 inches.

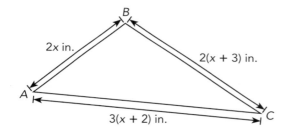

9. On a 3-week vacation to Paris, Martha's expenses on food, gifts, and accommodations was $80 less than three times her airfare. If the total expenses for the trip was $2,660, how much was her airfare?

10. Mark cycles from home to school at a speed of 16 kilometers per hour. He cycles back on the same route at a speed of 15 kilometers per hour. The total time taken for the journey is $7\frac{3}{4}$ hours. Given that the distance from his home to school is *d* kilometers, and that distance = speed · time, write and solve an equation to find the total distance traveled by him.

Lesson 4.4   Solving Algebraic Inequalities

Solve each inequality using the four operations. Then graph each solution set on a number line.

1. $27 + y < 10$

2. $4x + 5 \geq 29$

3. $6y + 1 > 7$

4. $3p + 1 \leq -1$

5. $9 \geq 12 - x$

6. $3 - 5x > 13$

7. $\frac{5}{6}x - \frac{1}{2} < \frac{1}{3}$

8. $\frac{7}{8} - \frac{1}{4}x \geq \frac{3}{4}$

9. $\frac{4}{5}y - \frac{1}{5} > 3$

10. $3x + 3 > 7 + x$

Solve each inequality using the four operations.

11. $8 - x < 10 - 2x$

12. $11 + x \leq 7 + 5x$

13. $0.3x - 7 < 11 + 0.2x$

14. $2.8x + 7 \geq 4.8x + 9$

15. $11.3 - 0.5x > 12 - 0.4x$

16. $\dfrac{3}{4}x + \dfrac{3}{4} \geq \dfrac{1}{2}x + 12.4$

17. $\dfrac{4}{7}x + 3 < \dfrac{5}{7}x + 4$

18. $\dfrac{5}{6}x + \dfrac{1}{3} < \dfrac{2}{3}x + 1$

19. $3(y + 2) \leq 18$

20. $6(2y - 1) > 3.6$

21. $2(9 - x) \leq 16 - x$

22. $2(2y - 3) - 4 \geq y - 2$

23. $\dfrac{1}{6}(a - 1) > 2(a - 1)$

24. $7(2a - 3) \leq 5 - 2(3a - 1)$

25. $2(2y - 3) < 4 + 3(y - 2)$

26. $8 + 5(z - 4) < 2(z + 7)$

Lesson 4.5   Real-World Problems: Algebraic Inequalities

Solve. Show your work.

1. Reuben has scores of 70, 75, 83, and 80 on four Spanish quizzes. What score must he get on the next quiz to achieve an average of at least 80?

2. Howard is saving to buy a mountain bike that costs $245, excluding tax. He has already saved $28. What is the least amount of money Howard must save each week so that at the end of the 9th week, he has enough money to buy the bike? Round your answer to the nearest dollar.

3. When Jane uses her calling card overseas, the cost of a phone call is $0.75 for the first three minutes and $0.12 for each additional minute, thereafter. If Jane plans to spend at most $3.60 to make a call, find the greatest possible length of talk time. Round your answer to the nearest whole number.

4. To raise money for a children's charity, a company is selling hot air balloon rides. The cost of going on a balloon ride is a flat rate of $50 plus $15 per hour of flight time. If Mrs. Beckham plans to donate at most $85, find the number of hours she can spend in the balloon ride. Round your answer to the nearest hour.

5. East High School's student council plans to buy some stools and chairs for a new student center. They need to buy 25 more chairs than stools. The chairs cost $32 each and the stools cost $28 each. If the budget is $2,620, how many chairs can they buy?

Name: _____   Date: _____

 Brain @ Work

1. One integer is 15 more than $\frac{3}{4}$ of another integer. The sum of the integers is greater than 49. Find the least values for these two integers.

2. Josie plans to rent a photo booth for her graduation party. A rental company offers two plans, A and B, as shown in the table.

Plan A	Plan B
Flat fee of $210 + $10 per hour	Flat fee of $120 + $25 per hour

   Based on the two plans, how many hours would Josie have to rent the photo booth for Plan A to be a better option?

3. The admission fees to a movie are as follows.

Category	Admission Fee
Adult	$8.50
Child	$5.50

   On a certain Saturday, the number of adult tickets sold was $\frac{1}{3}$ of the number of children tickets sold. What was the greatest number of adult tickets sold if the box office receipts was not more than $3,190?

Name: _____   Date: _____

CHAPTER

5 Direct and Inverse Proportion

Lesson 5.1 Understanding Direct Proportion

Tell whether _y_ is directly proportional to _x_. If so, find the constant of proportionality. Then write a direct proportion equation.

1.

x	1	2	3
y	4	8	12

2.

x	2	4	6
y	160	120	80

3.

x	3	6	9
y	10	30	70

4.

x	2	4	6
y	40	80	120

Tell whether each equation represents a direct proportion. If so, identify the constant of proportionality.

5. $\frac{1}{4}y = 5x$

6. $3y + 7 = x$

7. $a = 1.2b$

8. $2.5p = q - 1.6$

Name: _____   Date: _____

Solve. Show your work.

9. The table shows the time, t hours, that a production line needs to make n calculators. Tell whether n is directly proportional to t. If so, give the constant of proportionality and tell what it represents in this situation. Then write a direct proportion equation.

Number of Hours (t hours)	12	24	30
Number of Calculators (n)	30	60	75

10. The table shows the distance traveled by a car, d miles, after t hours. Tell whether d is directly proportional to t. If so, give the constant of proportionality and tell what it represents in this situation. Then write a direct proportion equation.

Time (t hours)	1	2	3
Distance Traveled (d miles)	50	110	200

11. The admission fee to a museum is $8.50 per person. Given that the admission fee, C dollars, is directly proportional to the number of people, n, identify the constant of proportionality and write a direct proportion equation.

12. A baker requires 21 ounces of flour to make a loaf of bread. Given that the amount of flour the baker needs, w ounces, is directly proportional to the number of loaves that he bakes, n, identify the constant of proportionality and write a direct proportion equation.

13. *a* is directly proportional to *b*, and *a* = 14 when *b* = 42. Write a direct proportion equation that relates *a* and *b*.

14. *w* is directly proportional to *v*, and *w* = 6 when *v* = 10. Write a direct proportion equation that relates *w* and *v*.

15. The amount Byron earns is directly proportional to the number of hours he works. If Byron earns $60.80 for 4 hours of work, find the constant of proportionality and write a direct proportion equation.

16. For every three minutes a faucet drips, one cup of water is wasted. The amount of water wasted is directly proportional to the amount of time the faucet drips. Find the constant of proportionality and write a direct proportion equation.

Lesson 5.2   Representing Direct Proportion Graphically

Tell whether each graph represents a direct proportion. If so, find the constant of proportionality.

1.

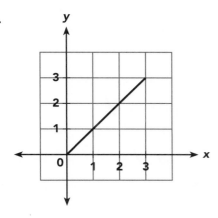

_____

2.

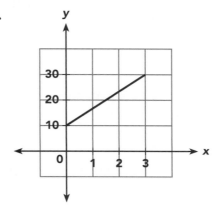

_____

3.

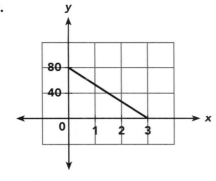

_____

4.

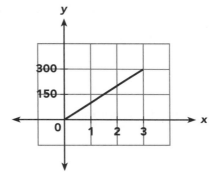

_____

5.

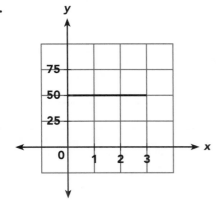

_____

6.

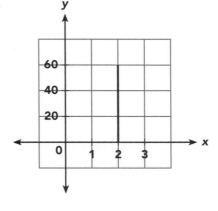

_____

Name: _____   Date: _____

Solve. Show your work.

7. The amount of money Joe earns is directly proportional to
   the number of hours he works. The graph shows the amount
   of money, *w* dollars, Joe earns in *t* hours.
   a) Find the constant of proportionality. What does this
   value represent in this situation?

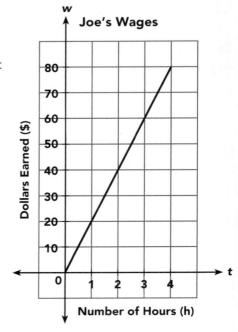

   b) How much does Joe earn if he works 3 hours?

   c) How long does Joe work if he earns $90?

8. The height of a seedling is directly proportional to the
   number of days since it was planted. The graph shows the
   height of the seedling, *h* centimeters, after *x* days.
   a) Find the constant of proportionality. What does this
   value represent in this situation?

   b) Write the direct proportion
   equation.

   c) Explain what the point (5, 10)
   represents in this situation.

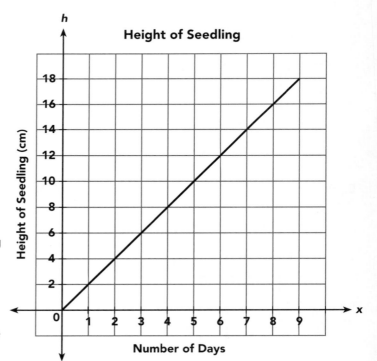

   d) What is the height of the seedling
   after 3 days? After one week?

   e) How many days will it take for the
   seedling to reach a height of at
   least 18 centimeters?

9. The amount of Japanese yen you get depends on the number of
U.S. dollars you exchange. Graph the relationship between y Japanese yen
and x U.S. dollars. Use 1 unit on the horizontal axis to represent 1 U.S. dollar
and 1 unit on the vertical axis to represent 80 Japanese yen.

U.S. dollars (x)	0	2	4	6	8
Japanese yen (y)	0	160	320	480	640

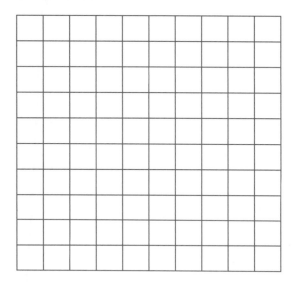

a) Does the amount of Japanese yen vary directly with the amount of
U.S. dollars?

b) What is the exchange rate when you convert U.S. dollars to
Japanese yen?

c) Write the direct proportion equation.

d) Yuki exchanges 480 Japanese yen for U.S. dollars. What amount
in U.S. dollars does she receive?

e) Justin exchanges 9 U.S. dollars for Japanese yen. What amount
in Japanese yen does he receive?

Lesson 5.3   Solving Direct Proportion Problems

Write a direct variation equation and find the indicated value.

1. *a* varies directly as *b*, and *a* = 4 when *b* = 24.
   a) Write an equation that relates *a* and *b*.

   b) Find *a* when *b* = 63.

   c) Find *b* when *a* = 7.

2. *w* varies directly as *v*, and *w* = 32 when *v* = 80.
   a) Write an equation that relates *w* and *v*.

   b) Find *w* when *v* = 120.

   c) Find *v* when *w* = 25.

3. *y* varies directly as *x*, and *y* = 18 when $x = \frac{1}{2}$.
   a) Write an equation that relates *y* and *x*.

   b) Find *x* when *y* = 252.

   c) Find *y* when $x = \frac{1}{3}$.

In each table, _p_ is directly proportional to _q_. Complete the following tables.

4.

_p_	20	40	?
_q_	4	?	16

5.

_p_	1	3	?
_q_	?	27	90

Solve. Show your work.

6. The cost of baseball caps, _C_ dollars, is directly proportional to the number of baseball caps, _n_, purchased. Eric purchased 12 baseball caps for $96.

   a) Find the cost of a baseball cap.

   b) Write an equation that relates _C_ and _n_.

   c) Find the value of _C_ when _n_ = 20.

7. The amount of money donated at a charity fundraising event, _A_, is directly proportional to the number of people, _n_, at the event. 6 people at the event donated a total of $120.

   a) Find the amount donated by each person at the event.

   b) Write an equation that relates the amount of money donated, _A_, and the number of people at the event, _n_.

   c) How much money did 50 people at the event donate?

8. Elizabeth can type 275 words in 5 minutes. The number of words she types, w, is directly proportional to the length of time she takes to type, t minutes.

   a) Find the constant of proportionality.

   b) Write an equation that relates w and t.

   c) How many minutes will it take her to type a 935-word document?

9. Johnny needs to determine the height of each tree on his tree farm. He knows that the height of the tree, h feet, is directly proportional to the length of its shadow, d feet. The length of a shadow cast by a 8-foot tall tree is 5 feet.

   a) Find the constant of proportionality.

   b) Write an equation that relates the height, h, of the tree and the length of its shadow, d.

   c) Use your equation to find the height of a tree that casts a shadow 12 feet long.

Use a proportion to solve each question. Show your work.

10. 4 cans of grapefruit juice cost $3.36. Find the cost of one dozen cans of grapefruit juice.

11. It costs $78 to rent a set of skis for 3 days. Find the cost of renting the skis for a week.

12. Elliot rides his bike at an average speed of 14 miles per hour. How many miles will he ride in $2\frac{1}{2}$ hours?

13. To make fruit punch, Susannah mixes lemonade with orange juice in the ratio 5 : 9. She uses 40 ounces of lemonade. How many ounces of orange juice does she use?

14. A machine can print 80 T-shirts in 10 minutes. Find the number of T-shirts the machine can print in an hour.

15. Jack buys a pair of shoes for $52 and pays $2.60 sales tax. How much sales tax will his friend pay if his friend purchases a shirt for $28?

16. A company invests $50,000 in a savings account that pays 3% interest per year.
   a) Write a direct proportion equation that relates interest, I, and years, t.

   b) How much interest will the company earn in 2 years?

17. Janet works at a computer supply store and earns 4.5% commission on her total sales. Last week, she earned $130.50 in commission. Calculate her total sales for last week.

18. In an experiment, Peter mixes vinegar with a salt solution in the ratio 3 : 7. How many ounces of vinegar are needed to mix with 35 ounces of salt solution?

19. A machine can pack 60 packets of pasta in 5 minutes.
 a) How long does it take the machine to pack 240 packets of pasta?

 b) How many packets of pasta can the machine pack in an hour?

20. The cost of a piece of vacant land in New York City, C dollars, is directly proportional to the area of the land, a square feet. If a 2,000-square foot vacant lot cost $129,920, find the cost for a 3,600-square foot vacant lot.

Lesson 5.4   Understanding Inverse Proportion

Tell whether two quantities are in inverse proportion. If so, find the constant of proportionality.

1.

x	100	50	10
y	2	4	20

2.

x	6	4	2
y	20	40	80

3.

x	3	6	9
y	10	20	30

4.

x	2	6	10
y	210	70	42

Tell whether each equation represents an inverse proportion. If so, give the constant of proportionality.

5. $y = 15x$

6. $xy = \dfrac{1}{4}$

7. $20y = \dfrac{4}{x}$

8. $xy + 3 = 7$

Each graph represents an inverse proportion. Find the constant of proportionality.

9.

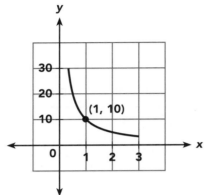

The constant of proportionality is _____.

10.

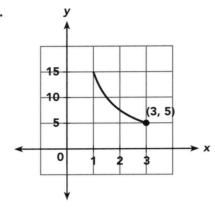

The constant of proportionality is _____.

11.

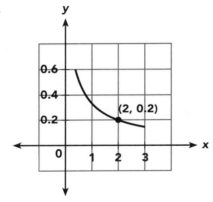

The constant of proportionality is _____.

12.

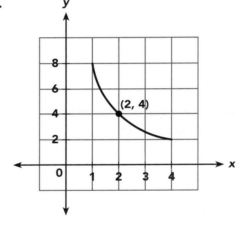

The constant of proportionality is _____.

13.

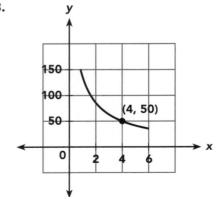

The constant of proportionality is _____.

14.

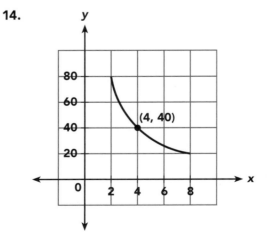

The constant of proportionality is _____.

Name: _____   Date: _____

Solve. Show your work.

15. s is inversely proportional to t, and $s = 12$ when $t = 7$.
    a)   Find the constant of proportionality.

    b)   Write an inverse equation relating s and t.

    c)   Find the value of s when $t = 5$.

16. y is inversely proportional to x, and $y = 6$ when $x = 7.5$.
    a)   Find the constant of proportionality.

    b)   Write an inverse equation relating x and y.

    c)   Find the value of y when $x = 2$.

17. The density of a substance is the mass of the substance per unit of volume. The density of the element Americium is inversely proportional to its volume. The graph shows the relationship between the density of Americium, ρ grams per cubic centimeters, and its volume, v cubic centimeters.
    a)   Use the graph to determine the constant of proportionality. Then write an inverse proportion equation.

    b)   Explain what the constant of proportionality represents in this situation.

    c)   Explain what the point (3, 4) represents in this situation.

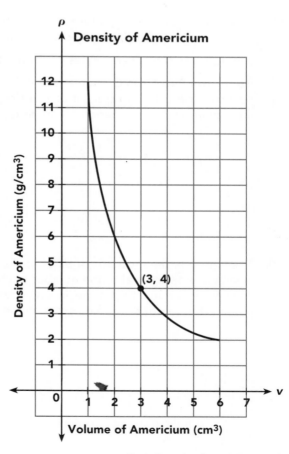

Density of Americium

Density of Americium (g/cm³)

Volume of Americium (cm³)

18. A tank has a fixed capacity. The time it takes to fill the empty tank, t minutes, is inversely proportional to the rate of water flowing into the tank, r pints per minute. The graph shows the relationship between r and t.

a) Use the graph to determine the constant of proportionality. Then write an inverse proportion equation.

b) Explain what the point (2, 300) represents in this situation.

c) How much time will it take to fill the empty tank if the water is flowing at a rate of 150 pints per minute?

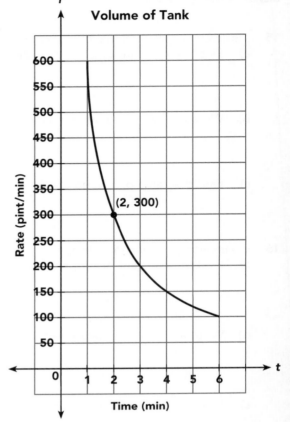

19. The number of hours, y, it takes to drive from Town P to Town Q is inversely proportional to the average speed of a car, x miles per hour. It takes Jeffrey $3\frac{1}{2}$ hours to drive from Town P to Town Q at an average speed of 60 miles per hour on a particular day. How long will it take Jeffrey to travel from Town P to Town Q if his average driving speed is 70 miles per hour instead?

20. The length of time, y hours, it takes to put a jigsaw puzzle together is inversely proportional to the number of children, x, working on it. It takes 16 children 6 hours to put the jigsaw puzzle together. How many children are needed to put the same jigsaw puzzle together in 4 hours?

Name: _____   Date: _____

Solve. Show your work.

1. The length of time it takes to tile a locker room floor, t hours, varies directly with the number of tiles needed, n, and varies inversely with the number of people laying the tiles, p.

a) Write an equation to represent the relationship. Use k for the constant of variation.

b) It takes 21 hours for 4 people to lay 1,500 tiles. Use your equation in **a)** to determine how long it will take 6 people to lay 5,000 tiles. Round your answer to the nearest whole hour.

2. The resistance, R, of a wire is directly proportional to the length of the wire, ℓ, and inversely proportional to the cross sectional area of the wire, A.

a) Write an equation to represent the relationship. Use k for the constant of proportionality.

b) Explain the effect on the resistance if the length of a wire is doubled.

c) Given that $A = \pi r^2$, where r is the radius of a wire, explain how the resistance is affected if the diameter, d, of the wire is doubled.

Cumulative Practice
for Chapters 3 to 5

Simplify each expression.

1. $5.8m + 2.3n - 4.9m - 1.7n$

2. $\frac{3}{7}x + \frac{5}{8} - \frac{3}{14}x + \frac{1}{4}$

Expand and simplify each expression.

3. $-0.6(x + 3y) - 0.4x$

4. $-\frac{1}{2}\left(\frac{2}{3}x - 4\right)$

5. $4\left(\frac{1}{5}x - 3y\right) + 7y - \frac{1}{3}x$

6. $-6(m + 3n) - 4(2m - n)$

Factor each expression.

7. $-9x - 45$

8. $18 - 30w + 6k$

Translate each verbal description into an algebraic expression. Simplify the expression when possible.

9. 45% of two-fifteenths of the product of $(x + 1)$ and one-twelfth y

10. Ten-ninths of the sum of $3x$, $12y$, and $-6z$

Name: _____   Date: _____

Tell whether each pair of equations are equivalent.

11. $5x + 1 = 11$ and $2x = 4$

12. $\frac{1}{3}y = 1$ and $y + 1 = 2$

Solve each equation.

13. $10.4 + 2.5y = 15.4$

14. $1.8(5 - 2y) = 0.9y$

15. $2(3p - 4) - 3(5 - 2p) + 18 = 19$

16. $9.6 - 2(4.5y + 3) = 1.2(2y - 3) + 3y$

Solve each inequality. Then graph each solution set on a number line.

17. $2 - 2(x - 3) > x - 7$

18. $m - \frac{1}{6}m - 1 \le \frac{1}{3}m + 1$

19. $11.8 - 0.7b < -9.2$

20. $7 - 4(5y - 3) \le 2(3 - y) - 5$

Tell whether each table, equation, or graph represents a direct proportion, an inverse proportion, or neither. Find the constant of proportionality for the direct and inverse proportion identified.

21.

x	0.2	0.6	1.2
y	3	9	18

22.

x	5	15	25
y	45	15	9

23.

x	20	40	60
y	−160	−320	−480

24. $y = \dfrac{1}{4}x + 5$

25. $0.5y = 3.5x$

26. $8y = \dfrac{72}{x}$

27.

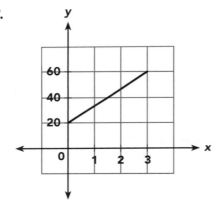

28.

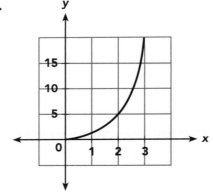

29.

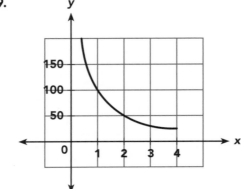

In each table, *y* is directly proportional to *x*. Find the constant of proportionality and then complete the table.

30.

x	5	10	
y		70	84

31.

x	100	200	
y	25		125

In each table, *y* is inversely proportional to *x*. Find the constant of proportionality and then complete the table.

32.

x	15	30	
y	60		20

33.

x		1	2	3
y			22.5	

Name: _____   Date: _____

Solve using proportional reasoning.

34. y varies directly as x, and $y = 4.5$ when $x = 0.5$.

   a) Write an equation that relates x and y.

   b) Find y when $x = 1.2$.

   c) Find x when $y = 7.2$.

35. P is inversely proportional to Q, and $P = 960$ when $Q = \dfrac{1}{3}$.

   a) Find the constant of proportionality.

   b) Write an equation that relates P and Q.

   c) Find P when $Q = \dfrac{1}{4}$.

   d) Find Q when $P = 16$.

Name: _____   Date: _____

Solve. Show your work.

36. The table shows the relationship between the gas usage, x gallons, and the distance traveled, y miles, of a car. Graph the relationship between the distance traveled, y, and the gas usage, x. Use 1 unit on the horizontal axis to represent 1 gallon and 1 unit on the vertical axis to represent 10 miles.

Gas usage (x gallons)	0	1	2	3	4	5
Distance traveled (y miles)	0	20	40	60	80	100

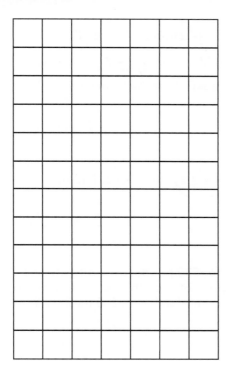

a) Is the distance traveled, in miles, directly proportional to the gas usage, in gallons? If so, find the constant of proportionality.

b) Owen will like to go to a town that is 100 miles away. How many gallons of gas does he need?

c) If 2 gallons of gas are left, how far can the car travel?

37. A man walked a distance of $(3x + 2y)$ meters for half an hour. He then continued to walk $\left(2x + \dfrac{1}{2}y\right)$ meters for another 20 minutes.

a) Determine the total distance he walked.

b) Find his average walking speed in meters per minute.

38. Ken, Leon, and Mark each collect seashells as a hobby. Ken has $(3x - 5)$ seashells, Leon has $(2x + 1)$ seashells, and Mark has $\left(\dfrac{1}{4}x + 7\right)$ seashells.

a) Write an expression for the total number of seashells they have collected in all.

b) If the total number of seashells collected by them is 45, find the number of seashells each of them has.

39. Catherine rents a booth at a flea market for $80 per day. She plans to sell printed T-shirts for $14 each. If the cost price of each shirt is $5, how many printed T-shirts must she sell to make a profit of at least $250 for a day?

40. A dozen cans of milk powder weigh 18 pounds. The weight of milk powder, w pounds, is directly proportional to the number of cans, n.
a) Find the constant of proportionality.

b) Write an equation that relates w and n.

c) What is the weight, in pounds, of 8 cans of milk powder?

41. A coin box contains quarters and dimes in the ratio of 4 : 5. The total number of coins in the box is $(6q + 18)$. Write an algebraic expression for each of the following.

 a) The number of dimes.

 b) The number of quarters.

 c) The total value of the coins in dollars.

42. Patricia bought 16 hairclips for \$3. x number of hairclips costs 15 cents each while the rest costs 20 cents each.

 a) Write an inequality in terms of x.

 b) Find the minimum number of 15-cent hairclips that she bought.

43. The number of days it takes to build a pavilion is inversely proportional to the number of carpenters. Given that 10 carpenters take 6 days to build the pavilion, how many more carpenters must be hired to complete building the same pavilion in 5 days?

44. The time it takes Johnny to drive from Town P to Town Q varies inversely as his average driving speed in miles per hour. The graph shows the relationship between x and y.

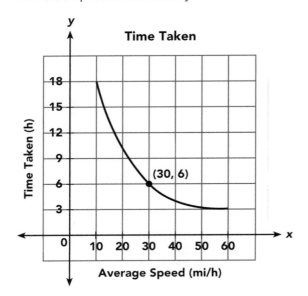

a) Find the constant of proportionality. Explain what it represents in this situation.

b) Write an equation that relates x and y.

c) Explain what the point (30, 6) represents in this situation.

d) How long does it take Johnny to reach Town Q if he travels at 60 miles per hour?

45. The diagram shows rectangle ABCD with a movable point P on $\overline{CD}$, such that the length of y can vary. Find the least value of y such that the area of triangle ABP is at least 27 square centimeters.

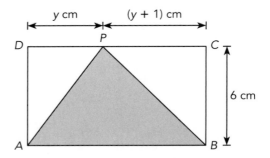

Answers

Chapter 1

Lesson 1.1

1. $\frac{3}{4}$

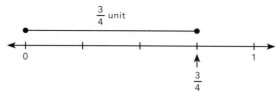

2. $\frac{47}{12}$

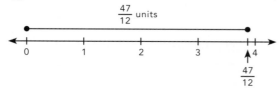

3. $-\frac{6}{13}$

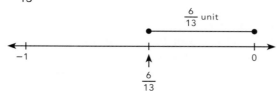

4. $-\frac{12}{5}$

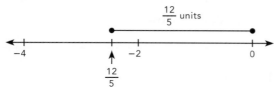

5. $\frac{12}{1}$

6. $-\frac{67}{1}, \frac{-67}{1},$ or $\frac{67}{-1}$

7. $\frac{5}{12}$

8. $\frac{375}{7}$

9. $\frac{59}{18}$

10. $-\frac{22}{21}, \frac{-22}{21},$ or $\frac{22}{-21}$

11. $\frac{37}{3}$

12. $-\frac{869}{12}, \frac{-869}{12},$ or $\frac{869}{-12}$

13. $\frac{1}{2}$

14. $\frac{251}{100}$

15. $\frac{699}{200}$

16. $-\frac{27}{200}, \frac{-27}{200},$ or $\frac{27}{-200}$

17. $-\frac{33}{25}, \frac{-33}{25},$ or $\frac{33}{-25}$

18. $-\frac{138}{25}, \frac{-138}{25},$ or $\frac{138}{-25}$

19.

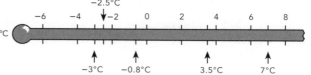

20.

21.

22.

23.

24.

25.

26.

27. $-4\frac{5}{14}, -\frac{22}{7}, -3.12, 1.01, \frac{21}{4}, 6.7$

Lesson 1.2

1. $\frac{7}{16} = 0.4375$

$$
\begin{array}{r}
0.4375 \\
16\overline{)7.0000} \\
\underline{6\ 4} \\
60 \\
\underline{48} \\
120 \\
\underline{112} \\
80 \\
\underline{80} \\
0
\end{array}
$$

2. $\frac{654}{15} = 43.6$

$$
\begin{array}{r}
43.6 \\
15\overline{)654.0} \\
\underline{60} \\
54 \\
\underline{45} \\
90 \\
\underline{90} \\
0
\end{array}
$$

3. $-\dfrac{9}{24} = -0.375$

$$
\begin{array}{r}
0.375 \\
24\overline{)9.000} \\
72 \\
\hline
180 \\
168 \\
\hline
120 \\
120 \\
\hline
0
\end{array}
$$

4. $-\dfrac{126}{35} = -3.6$

$$
\begin{array}{r}
3.6 \\
35\overline{)126.0} \\
105 \\
\hline
210 \\
210 \\
\hline
0
\end{array}
$$

5. $\dfrac{28}{9} = 3.\overline{1}$

$$
\begin{array}{r}
3.11 \\
9\overline{)28.00} \\
27 \\
\hline
10 \\
9 \\
\hline
10 \\
9 \\
\hline
1
\end{array}
$$

6. $8\dfrac{1}{15} = \dfrac{121}{15}$

$\qquad = 8.0\overline{6}$

$$
\begin{array}{r}
8.066 \\
15\overline{)121.000} \\
120 \\
\hline
100 \\
90 \\
\hline
100 \\
90 \\
\hline
10
\end{array}
$$

7. $-56\dfrac{5}{6} = -\dfrac{341}{6}$

$\qquad = -56.8\overline{3}$

$$
\begin{array}{r}
56.833 \\
6\overline{)341.000} \\
30 \\
\hline
41 \\
36 \\
\hline
50 \\
48 \\
\hline
20 \\
18 \\
\hline
20 \\
18 \\
\hline
2
\end{array}
$$

8. $-\dfrac{2}{11} = -0.\overline{18}$

$$
\begin{array}{r}
0.1818 \\
11\overline{)2.0000} \\
11 \\
\hline
90 \\
88 \\
\hline
20 \\
11 \\
\hline
90 \\
88 \\
\hline
2
\end{array}
$$

9. $0.\overline{45}$

10. $-0.\overline{692307}$

11. $-3.\overline{70731}$

12. $1.\overline{824175}$

13. $-2.6471, \ 4.7368, \ 6.3000, \ -1.5268, \ 4.7222$

14. $-2\dfrac{11}{17} < -\dfrac{171}{112} < 4\dfrac{13}{18} < \dfrac{90}{19} < \dfrac{63}{10}$

15.

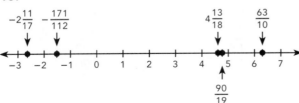

16. $\dfrac{63}{10}$

Lesson 1.3

1. $\sqrt{8}$ is between 2 and 3.

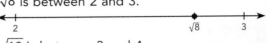

2. $\sqrt{10}$ is between 3 and 4.

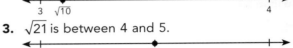

3. $\sqrt{21}$ is between 4 and 5.

4. $\sqrt{37}$ is between 6 and 7.

5. $-\sqrt{8}$ is between -2 and -3.

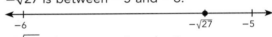

6. $-\sqrt{14}$ is between -3 and -4.

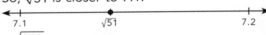

7. $-\sqrt{27}$ is between -5 and -6.

8. $-\sqrt{68}$ is between -8 and -9.

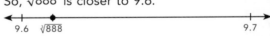

9. $\sqrt{51} = 7.141\ldots$
7.141 is closer to 7.1 than to 7.2.
So, $\sqrt{51}$ is closer to 7.1.

10. $-\sqrt{279} = -16.703\ldots$
-16.703 is closer to -16.7 than to -16.8.
So, $-\sqrt{279}$ is closer to -16.7.

11. $\sqrt[3]{888} = 9.612\ldots$
9.612 is closer to 9.6 than to 9.7.
So, $\sqrt[3]{888}$ is closer to 9.6.

12. $\sqrt{99} = 9.94987\ldots$
9.95 is closer to 9.9 than to 10.0.
So, $\sqrt{99}$ is closer to 9.9.

13. $-\sqrt{1999} = -44.71017\ldots$
-44.71 is closer to -44.7 than to -44.8.
So, $-\sqrt{1999}$ is closer to -44.7.

14. $\sqrt{6655} = 81.57818\ldots$
81.58 is closer to 81.6 than to 81.5.
So, $\sqrt{6655}$ is closer to 81.6.

15. $\pi^2 = 9.86960...$

π^2 is closer to 9.9 than to 9.8.

So, π^2 is closer to 9.9.

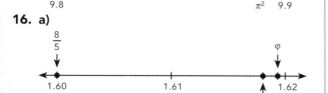

16. a)

b) 1.6175

17. $\sqrt[3]{130}$ in.; 5.07 in.

Lesson 1.4

1. <   **2.** >

3. <   **4.** >

5. 7.874, 9.997, 3.142, 1.345

6.

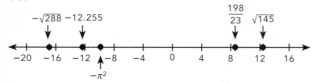

7. $\sqrt[3]{999} > \sqrt{62} > \pi > -1.\overline{345}$

8.

Rational Numbers	Irrational Numbers
$1.34; -4\frac{5}{12}; -\frac{31}{6}$	$\sqrt{37}; -\sqrt[3]{266}$

9. $-\sqrt[3]{266} < -\frac{31}{6} < -4\frac{5}{12} < 1.34 < \sqrt{37}$

10. 8.6087, −12.255, −9.8696, 12.0416, −16.9706

11.

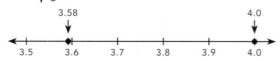

12.

Rational Numbers	Irrational Numbers
$\frac{198}{23}; -12.255$	$-\pi^2; \sqrt{145}; -\sqrt{288}$

13. a) 3.58 m/s

b) Yes; The speed now is greater than $\sqrt{\frac{64}{5}}$ m/s.

4 is further away from 0 than $\sqrt{\frac{64}{5}}$.

Lesson 1.5

1. 2, 6, 7, 0, and 1; 5

2. 7, 0, 0, 3, 1, and 1; 6

3. 1, 0, and 9; 3   **4.** 6, 8, and 0; 3

5. 5 and 2; 2   **6.** 7; 1

7. 5,000   **8.** 47,000

9. 6,390,000   **10.** 32,010,000

11. 0.09   **12.** −4.6

13. −2.00   **14.** −0.00985

15. 2.171   **16.** 761.11

17. a) 9,000,000   **b)** 8,700,000

     c) 8,710,000   **d)** 8,709,000

18. a) 46,010   **b)** 46,009

     c) 46,009.5   **d)** 46,009.49

19. 5

20. None of the trailing zeros are significant because the distance is a rounded value to the nearest 100,000.

21. The digit 7 is the least reliable.

22. 6,976,950,000

23. Average speed = 9.2635...m/s = $\frac{400}{43.18}$ m/s

The average speed, correct to 3 significant digits, is 9.26 meters per second.

24. a) 6.00, 6.40

b) Mean diameter

$$= \frac{6.00 + 6.40 + 5.75 + 5.25 + 5.36}{5}$$

= 5.752 mm

The mean of the diameters is 5.75 millimeters.

Brain@Work

1. Let the original number be 0.01y.
When the decimal places of the original number is moved four places to the right, the new number is 100y.

$$100y = 9 \cdot \frac{1}{0.01y}$$

$$= \frac{900}{y}$$

$$y = \frac{9}{y}$$

By trial and error, y = 3.
The original number is 0.03.

2. $\frac{a}{3}$ is at least 100 to form a three-digit number. So, a is at least 300.
The largest possible three-digit number that can be formed is 999. So, $2a$ is at most 999.
a is at most 499.5.
a is between 300 and 499.5 inclusive.
The total number of positive integers for $a = 100 + 99 + 1 = 200$.

Chapter 2

Lesson 2.1

1.

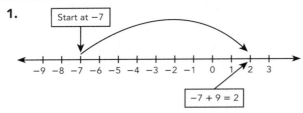

$-7 + 9 = 2$

2.

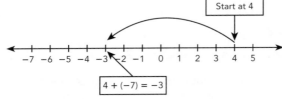

$4 + (-7) = -3$

3.

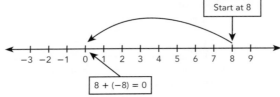

$8 + (-8) = 0$

4.

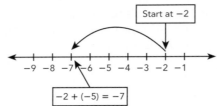

$-2 + (-5) = -7$

5.

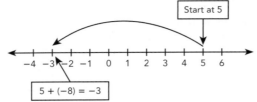

$5 + (-8) = -3$

6.

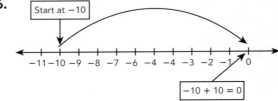

$-10 + 10 = 0$

7. $|18| = 18$
$|-39| = 39$
$|-39| - |18| = 39 - 18$
$\qquad\qquad\quad = 21$
Use a negative sign, because -39 has a greater absolute value.
$18 + (-39) = -21$

8. $|62| = 62$
$|-18| = 18$
$|62| - |-18| = 62 - 18$
$\qquad\qquad\quad = 44$
The sum is positive, because 62 has a greater absolute value.
$62 + (-18) = 44$

9. $|-25| = 25$
$|14| = 14$
$|-25| - |14| = 25 - 14$
$\qquad\qquad\quad = 11$
Use a negative sign, because -25 has a greater absolute value.
$-25 + 14 = -11$

10. $|-43| = 43$
$|72| = 72$
$|72| - |-43| = 72 - 43$
$\qquad\qquad\quad = 29$
The sum is positive, because 72 has a greater absolute value.
$-43 + 72 = 29$

11. $|-19| = 19$
$|-32| = 32$
$|-32| + |-19| = 32 + 19$
$\qquad\qquad\qquad = 51$
Use the common sign, a negative sign, for the sum.
$-19 + (-32) = -51$

12. $|-57| = 57$
$|-21| = 21$
$|-57| + |-21| = 57 + 21$
$\qquad\qquad\qquad = 78$
Use the common sign, a negative sign, for the sum.
$-57 + (-21) = -78$

13. $-7 + 12 + 9$
$= -7 + 21$
$= 14$

14. $-88 + 35 + 27$
$= -88 + 62$
$= -26$

15. $14 + (-20) + (-6)$
$= 14 + (-26)$
$= -12$

16. $-31 + (-5) + 12$
$= -36 + 12$
$= -24$

17. $-45 + (-27) + (-41)$
$= -72 + (-41)$
$= -113$

18. $16 + (-54) + 23$
$= 16 + 23 + (-54)$
$= 39 + (-54)$
$= -15$

19. $-340 + 76 = -264$ ft
The depth of the submarine will be 264 feet below sea level.

20. $-320 + 23 = -297°F$
The boiling point of oxygen is $-297°F$.

21. $50 + (-85) + (-12) + 93$
$= 50 + 93 + (-85) + (-12)$
$= 143 + (-97)$
$= 46$ points
His final score is 46 points.

22. Price of stock after day 1: $26 - $5 = $21
Price of stock after day 2: $21 - $2 = $19
Price of stock after day 3: $19 + $1 = $20
Price of stock after day 4: $20 - $6 = $14
The stock was worth $14 at the end of day 4.

23. $-3 + 18 = 15°F$
The temperature at noon is 15°F.

Lesson 2.2

1. $9 - 11 = 9 + (-11)$
$= -2$

2. $46 - 87 = 46 + (-87)$
$= -41$

3. $30 - 40 = 30 + (-40)$
$= -10$

4. $28 - (-15) = 28 + 15$
$= 43$

5. $-14 - (-12) = -14 + 12$
$= -2$

6. $-113 - (-58) = -113 + 58$
$= -55$

7. $-5 - 17 - 23 = -5 + (-17) - 23$
$= -22 - 23$
$= -22 + (-23)$
$= -45$

8. $-3 - (-6) - 10 = -3 + 6 - 10$
$= 3 - 10$
$= 3 + (-10)$
$= -7$

9. $-8 - (-12) - 31 = -8 + 12 - 31$
$= 4 - 31$
$= 4 + (-31)$
$= -27$

10. $-47 - (-20) - (-67) = -47 + 20 + 67$
$= -27 + 67$
$= 40$

11. $-93 - (-17) - (-53) = -93 + 17 + 53$
$= -76 + 53$
$= -23$

12. $-16 - (-9) - (-16) = -16 + 9 + 16$
$= -7 + 16$
$= 9$

13. Distance between 8 and 32:
$|8 - 32| = |8 + (-32)|$
$= 24$ units

14. Distance between 15 and 64:
$|15 - 64| = |15 + (-64)|$
$= 49$ units

15. Distance between -27 and 18:
$|-27 - 18| = 45$ units

16. Distance between -9 and 35:
$|-9 - 35| = 44$ units

17. Distance between -24 and -11:
$|-24 - (-11)| = |-24 + 11|$
$= 13$ units

18. Distance between -7 and -35:
$|-7 - (-35)| = |-7 + 35|$
$= 28$ units

19. $-6 - 8 = -14°C$
The new temperature is $-14°C$.

20. $-28 + (-35) = -63$ ft
His new depth is 63 feet below the sea level.

21. $|49 - (-54)| = |49 + 54|$
$= 103°F$
The temperature difference is 103°F.

22. $|20,320 - (-282)| = |20,320 + 282|$
$= 20,602$ ft
The difference in elevation is 20,602 feet.

23. $|134 - (-129)| = |134 + 129|$
$= 263°F$
The difference between these temperatures is 263°F.

24. $-31 - 27 = -31 + (-27)$
$= -58°F$
The record low in South Dakota was $-58°F$.

25. 480 − 570 = 480 + (−570)
$\qquad$ = −90
Simon's final score was −90 points.

Lesson 2.3

1. 7 · (−9) = −63 $\qquad$ **2.** 12 · (−8) = −96

3. −3 · 11= −33 $\qquad$ **4.** −5 · 6 = −30

5. −6 · (−8) = 48 $\qquad$ **6.** −7 · (−15) = 105

7. −30 · (0) = 0 $\qquad$ **8.** 0 · (−19) = 0

9. 4 · (−6) · (10) = −24 · 10
$\qquad$ = −240

10. 7 · 8 · (−9) = 56 · (−9)
$\qquad$ = −504

11. −11(5)(−4) = −55 · (−4)
$\qquad$ = 220

12. −2(−21)(3) = 42 · 3
$\qquad$ = 126

13. 6(−14)(−17) = −84 · (−17)
$\qquad$ = 1,428

14. −4(−28)(−9) = 112 · (−9)
$\qquad$ = −1,008

15. −3(−12)(−10) = 36 · (−10)
$\qquad$ = −360

16. −8(0)(−27) = 0

17. −50(−6)(0) = 0

18. −9(−8)(2)(3) = 72 · 2 · 3
$\qquad$ = 144 · 3
$\qquad$ = 432

19. −5(7)(−4)(−5) = −35 · (−4) · (−5)
$\qquad$ = 140 · (−5)
$\qquad$ = −700

20. −10(−3)(−6)(−2) = 30 · (−6) · (−2)
$\qquad$ = −180 · (−2)
$\qquad$ = 360

21. 357 ÷ (−7) = −51 $\quad$ **22.** 560 ÷ (−16) = −35

23. −720 ÷ 12 = −60 $\quad$ **24.** −550 ÷ 11 = −50

25. −189 ÷ (−9) = 21 $\quad$ **26.** −112 ÷ (−4) = 28

27. 0 ÷ (−20) = 0 $\qquad$ **28.** 0 ÷ (−5) = 0

29. Change in altitude per minute
$\qquad$ = −2,250 ÷ 15
$\qquad$ = −150 ft/min
The change in altitude per minute is
−150 ft per/min.

30. Distance = −2 · 40
$\qquad$ = −80 ft
He is 80 feet below sea level after 40 minutes.

31. Average change in sales income per
month = $9,000,000 ÷ 3
$\qquad$ = $3,000,000
The average change in sales income is
$3,000,000 per month.

32. Total change in the stock's value
$\qquad$ = −2 · 7 = −$14
The total change in the stock's value is −$14.

Lesson 2.4

1. −5 · 8 + 12 $\qquad$ **2.** 20 − 4 · −6
$\quad$ = −40 + 12 $\qquad\qquad$ = 20 − (−24)
$\quad$ = −28 $\qquad\qquad\qquad$ = 20 + 24
$\qquad\qquad\qquad\qquad\qquad$ = 44

3. 3 · (−9) + (−2) · 7 $\quad$ **4.** 150 ÷ (−5) + (−38)
$\quad$ = −27 + (−14) $\qquad\qquad$ = −30 + (−38)
$\quad$ = −41 $\qquad\qquad\qquad$ = −68

5. −48 ÷ 4 · (−5) − 17
$\quad$ = −48 ÷ (−20) − 17
$\quad$ = 2.4 − 17
$\quad$ = −14.6

6. −35 − 490 ÷ 7 + 12
$\quad$ = −35 − 70 + 12
$\quad$ = −105 + 12
$\quad$ = −93

7. 82 − (9 − 13) · 9
$\quad$ = 82 − (−4) · 9
$\quad$ = 82 − (−36)
$\quad$ = 82 + 36
$\quad$ = 118

8. −27 − (4 + 4) · 3
$\quad$ = −27 − 8 · 3
$\quad$ = −27 − 24
$\quad$ = −51

9. 90 ÷ (−6 − 3) + 45
$\quad$ = 90 ÷ (−9) + 45
$\quad$ = −10 + 45
$\quad$ = 35

10. (16 + 2)(3) − 5(−5 + 3)
$\quad$ = (18)(3) − 5(−2)
$\quad$ = 54 − (−10)
$\quad$ = 54 + 10
$\quad$ = 64

11. −30 + 5(3 + 8) − 45
$\quad$ = −30 + 5(11) − 45
$\quad$ = −30 + 55 − 45
$\quad$ = −75 + 55
$\quad$ = −20

12. 25 ÷ [−4 + (−1)] − 9(3)
$\quad$ = 25 ÷ (−5) − 9(3)
$\quad$ = 25 ÷ (−5) − 27
$\quad$ = −5 − 27
$\quad$ = −32

13. 36 ÷ 6 − (−25 + 15)(4)
$\quad$ = 36 ÷ 6 − (−10)(4)
$\quad$ = 36 ÷ 6 − (−40)
$\quad$ = 6 − (−40)
$\quad$ = 6 + 40
$\quad$ = 46

14. $-42 + 70 \div (-2 - 3) + 84 \div (4 + 2)$
$= -42 + 70 \div (-5) + 84 \div 6$
$= -42 - 14 + 14$
$= -42 + 0$
$= -42$

15. $-200 + 32\,(-3 + 7) - 45(15 - 20)$
$= -200 + 32(4) - 45 \cdot (-5)$
$= -200 + 128 - (-225)$
$= -200 + 128 + 225$
$= -72 + 225$
$= 153$

16. $480 \div (6 + 14) - 7 \cdot (4) + 8 \cdot (3 + 4)$
$= 480 \div 20 - 7 \cdot 4 + 8 \cdot 7$
$= 480 \div 20 - 28 + 56$
$= 24 - 28 + 56$
$= -4 + 56$
$= 52$

17. Area of remaining paper:
Area of original paper − Area of two cut-out triangles − Area of two cut-out rectangles
$= 12 \cdot 8 - 2 \cdot \dfrac{1}{2} \cdot 4 \cdot 4 - 2 \cdot 4 \cdot 3$
$= 96 - 16 - 24$
$= 56 \text{ in}^2$
The area of the remaining paper is 56 square inches.

18. Volume of water pumped out over 3 days
$= 3 \cdot 210$
$= 630 \text{ gal}$
Water volume 3 days ago $= 6{,}600 + 630$
$\qquad\qquad\qquad\qquad\quad = 7{,}230 \text{ gal}$

The volume of water in the tank 3 days ago was 7,230 gallons.

Lesson 2.5

1. $-\dfrac{8}{3} + \dfrac{1}{4} = -\dfrac{8 \cdot 4}{3 \cdot 4} + \dfrac{1 \cdot 3}{4 \cdot 3}$
$\qquad\qquad\quad = -\dfrac{32}{12} + \dfrac{3}{12}$
$\qquad\qquad\quad = \dfrac{-32 + 3}{12}$
$\qquad\qquad\quad = \dfrac{-29}{12}$
$\qquad\qquad\quad = -2\dfrac{5}{12}$

2. $\dfrac{4}{15} + \left(-\dfrac{7}{9}\right) = \dfrac{4}{15} - \dfrac{7}{9}$
$\qquad\qquad\quad = \dfrac{4 \cdot 3}{15 \cdot 3} - \dfrac{7 \cdot 5}{9 \cdot 5}$
$\qquad\qquad\quad = \dfrac{12}{45} - \dfrac{35}{45}$
$\qquad\qquad\quad = \dfrac{12 - 35}{45}$
$\qquad\qquad\quad = -\dfrac{23}{45}$

3. $-\dfrac{7}{15} + \dfrac{4}{5} = \dfrac{-7}{15} + \dfrac{4 \cdot 3}{5 \cdot 3}$
$\qquad\qquad\quad = \dfrac{-7}{15} + \dfrac{12}{15}$
$\qquad\qquad\quad = \dfrac{-7 + 12}{15}$
$\qquad\qquad\quad = \dfrac{5}{15}$
$\qquad\qquad\quad = \dfrac{1}{3}$

4. $\dfrac{-5}{8} + \left(-\dfrac{1}{3}\right) = \dfrac{-5}{8} - \dfrac{1}{3}$
$\qquad\qquad\quad = \dfrac{-5 \cdot 3}{8 \cdot 3} - \dfrac{1 \cdot 8}{3 \cdot 8}$
$\qquad\qquad\quad = \dfrac{-15}{24} - \dfrac{8}{24}$
$\qquad\qquad\quad = \dfrac{-15 - 8}{24}$
$\qquad\qquad\quad = -\dfrac{23}{24}$

5. $\dfrac{2}{3} - \left(-\dfrac{5}{9}\right) = \dfrac{2}{3} + \dfrac{5}{9}$
$\qquad\qquad\quad = \dfrac{2 \cdot 3}{3 \cdot 3} + \dfrac{5}{9}$
$\qquad\qquad\quad = \dfrac{6}{9} + \dfrac{5}{9}$
$\qquad\qquad\quad = \dfrac{6 + 5}{9}$
$\qquad\qquad\quad = \dfrac{11}{9}$
$\qquad\qquad\quad = 1\dfrac{2}{9}$

6. $\dfrac{1}{6} - \left(\dfrac{-2}{3}\right) = \dfrac{1}{6} + \dfrac{2}{3}$
$\qquad\qquad\quad = \dfrac{1}{6} + \dfrac{2 \cdot 2}{3 \cdot 2}$
$\qquad\qquad\quad = \dfrac{1}{6} + \dfrac{4}{6}$
$\qquad\qquad\quad = \dfrac{1 + 4}{6}$
$\qquad\qquad\quad = \dfrac{5}{6}$

7. $-\dfrac{1}{5} - \dfrac{2}{15} = -\dfrac{1 \cdot 3}{5 \cdot 3} - \dfrac{2}{15}$
$\qquad\qquad\quad = -\dfrac{3}{15} - \dfrac{2}{15}$
$\qquad\qquad\quad = \dfrac{-3 - 2}{15}$
$\qquad\qquad\quad = \dfrac{-5}{15}$
$\qquad\qquad\quad = -\dfrac{1}{3}$

8. $\dfrac{-1}{7} - \dfrac{3}{14} = \dfrac{-1 \cdot 2}{7 \cdot 2} - \dfrac{3}{14}$

$\qquad = \dfrac{-2}{14} - \dfrac{3}{14}$

$\qquad = \dfrac{-2 - 3}{14}$

$\qquad = -\dfrac{5}{14}$

9. $\dfrac{-3}{4} - \left(-\dfrac{1}{2}\right) = \dfrac{-3}{4} + \dfrac{1 \cdot 2}{2 \cdot 2}$

$\qquad = \dfrac{-3}{4} + \dfrac{2}{4}$

$\qquad = \dfrac{-3 + 2}{4}$

$\qquad = -\dfrac{1}{4}$

10. $-\dfrac{2}{5} - \left(\dfrac{-3}{4}\right) - \dfrac{5}{8} = -\dfrac{2}{5} + \dfrac{3}{4} - \dfrac{5}{8}$

$\qquad = -\dfrac{2 \cdot 8}{5 \cdot 8} + \dfrac{3 \cdot 10}{4 \cdot 10} - \dfrac{5 \cdot 5}{8 \cdot 5}$

$\qquad = -\dfrac{16}{40} + \dfrac{30}{40} - \dfrac{25}{40}$

$\qquad = \dfrac{-16 + 30 - 25}{40}$

$\qquad = -\dfrac{11}{40}$

11. $\dfrac{1}{3} - \left(-\dfrac{2}{5}\right) - \dfrac{3}{4} = \dfrac{1}{3} + \dfrac{2}{5} - \dfrac{3}{4}$

$\qquad = \dfrac{1 \cdot 20}{3 \cdot 20} + \dfrac{2 \cdot 12}{5 \cdot 12} - \dfrac{3 \cdot 15}{4 \cdot 15}$

$\qquad = \dfrac{20}{60} + \dfrac{24}{60} - \dfrac{45}{60}$

$\qquad = \dfrac{20 + 24 - 45}{60}$

$\qquad = -\dfrac{1}{60}$

12. $\dfrac{-2}{9} - \left(\dfrac{-1}{3}\right) - \left(\dfrac{-3}{5}\right) = \dfrac{-2}{9} + \dfrac{1}{3} + \dfrac{3}{5}$

$\qquad = \dfrac{-2 \cdot 5}{9 \cdot 5} + \dfrac{1 \cdot 15}{3 \cdot 15} + \dfrac{3 \cdot 9}{5 \cdot 9}$

$\qquad = \dfrac{-10}{45} + \dfrac{15}{45} + \dfrac{27}{45}$

$\qquad = \dfrac{-10 + 15 + 27}{45}$

$\qquad = \dfrac{32}{45}$

13. $-\dfrac{5}{6} + \left(\dfrac{-3}{4}\right) + \dfrac{5}{8} = -\dfrac{5}{6} - \dfrac{3}{4} + \dfrac{5}{8}$

$\qquad = \dfrac{-5 \cdot 4}{6 \cdot 4} - \dfrac{3 \cdot 6}{4 \cdot 6} + \dfrac{5 \cdot 3}{8 \cdot 3}$

$\qquad = \dfrac{-20}{24} - \dfrac{18}{24} + \dfrac{15}{24}$

$\qquad = \dfrac{-20 - 18 + 15}{24}$

$\qquad = -\dfrac{23}{24}$

14. $\dfrac{-4}{9} + \left(\dfrac{-5}{6}\right) + \left(\dfrac{-1}{3}\right) = -\dfrac{4}{9} - \dfrac{5}{6} - \dfrac{1}{3}$

$\qquad = -\dfrac{4 \cdot 2}{9 \cdot 2} - \dfrac{5 \cdot 3}{6 \cdot 3} - \dfrac{1 \cdot 6}{3 \cdot 6}$

$\qquad = \dfrac{-8}{18} - \dfrac{15}{18} - \dfrac{6}{18}$

$\qquad = \dfrac{-8 - 15 - 6}{18}$

$\qquad = -\dfrac{29}{18}$

$\qquad = -1\dfrac{11}{18}$

15. $-\dfrac{3}{4} \cdot \dfrac{5}{12} = \dfrac{-{}^1\!\cancel{3} \cdot 5}{4 \cdot \cancel{12}_4}$

$\qquad = -\dfrac{5}{16}$

16. $-2\dfrac{1}{4} \cdot \dfrac{8}{27} = -\dfrac{9}{4} \cdot \dfrac{8}{27}$

$\qquad = \dfrac{-{}^1\!\cancel{9} \cdot \cancel{8}^{\,2}}{{}_1\cancel{4} \cdot \cancel{27}_3}$

$\qquad = -\dfrac{2}{3}$

17. $-\dfrac{14}{25} \cdot \left(-1\dfrac{3}{7}\right) = -\dfrac{14}{25} \cdot \left(-\dfrac{10}{7}\right)$

$\qquad = \dfrac{{}^2\cancel{14} \cdot \cancel{10}^{\,2}}{{}_5\cancel{25} \cdot \cancel{7}_1}$

$\qquad = \dfrac{4}{5}$

18. $1\dfrac{8}{27} \cdot \left(-2\dfrac{2}{5}\right) = \dfrac{35}{27} \cdot \left(-\dfrac{12}{5}\right)$

$\qquad = \dfrac{{}^7\cancel{35} \cdot -\cancel{12}^{\,4}}{{}_9\cancel{27} \cdot \cancel{5}_1}$

$\qquad = -\dfrac{28}{9}$

$\qquad = -3\dfrac{1}{9}$

19. $-2\dfrac{2}{3} \cdot \left(-3\dfrac{3}{4}\right) = -\dfrac{8}{3} \cdot \left(-\dfrac{15}{4}\right)$

$\qquad = \dfrac{{}^2\cancel{8} \cdot \cancel{15}^{\,5}}{{}_1\cancel{3} \cdot \cancel{4}_1}$

$\qquad = 10$

20. $\dfrac{2}{15} \cdot \left(-1\dfrac{2}{3}\right) = \dfrac{2}{15} \cdot \left(-\dfrac{5}{3}\right)$

$\qquad = \dfrac{2 \cdot -\cancel{5}^{\,1}}{_3\cancel{15} \cdot 3}$

$\qquad = -\dfrac{2}{9}$

21. $-\dfrac{1}{4} \div \dfrac{3}{8} = -\dfrac{1}{4} \cdot \dfrac{8}{3}$

$\qquad = \dfrac{-1 \cdot \cancel{8}^{\,2}}{_1\cancel{4} \cdot 3}$

$\qquad = -\dfrac{2}{3}$

22. $\dfrac{2}{5} \div \left(-\dfrac{4}{35}\right) = \dfrac{2}{5} \cdot \left(-\dfrac{35}{4}\right)$

$\qquad = \dfrac{^1\cancel{2} \cdot -\cancel{35}^{\,7}}{_1\cancel{5} \cdot \cancel{4}_2}$

$\qquad = -\dfrac{7}{2}$

$\qquad = -3\dfrac{1}{2}$

23. $-\dfrac{1}{6} \div \left(-\dfrac{5}{18}\right) = -\dfrac{1}{6} \cdot \left(-\dfrac{18}{5}\right)$

$\qquad = \dfrac{1 \cdot \cancel{18}^{\,3}}{_1\cancel{6} \cdot 5}$

$\qquad = \dfrac{3}{5}$

24. $1\dfrac{2}{3} \div \left(-3\dfrac{1}{3}\right) = \dfrac{5}{3} \div \left(-\dfrac{10}{3}\right)$

$\qquad = \dfrac{5}{3} \cdot \left(-\dfrac{3}{10}\right)$

$\qquad = \dfrac{^1\cancel{5} \cdot -\cancel{3}^{\,1}}{_1\cancel{3} \cdot \cancel{10}_2}$

$\qquad = -\dfrac{1}{2}$

25. $-2\dfrac{3}{4} \div \left(-1\dfrac{3}{8}\right) = \left(-\dfrac{11}{4}\right) \div \left(-\dfrac{11}{8}\right)$

$\qquad = -\dfrac{11}{4} \cdot \left(-\dfrac{8}{11}\right)$

$\qquad = \dfrac{^1\cancel{11} \cdot \cancel{8}^{\,2}}{_1\cancel{4} \cdot \cancel{11}_1}$

$\qquad = 2$

26. $\dfrac{-10}{\left(\dfrac{5}{13}\right)} = -10 \div \dfrac{5}{13}$

$\qquad = -10 \cdot \dfrac{13}{5}$

$\qquad = \dfrac{^{-2}\cancel{10} \cdot 13}{1 \cdot \cancel{5}_1}$

$\qquad = -26$

27. $\dfrac{\left(\dfrac{2}{3}\right)}{-16} = \dfrac{2}{3} \div (-16)$

$\qquad = \dfrac{^1\cancel{2}}{3} \cdot \dfrac{1}{-\cancel{16}_8}$

$\qquad = -\dfrac{1}{24}$

28. $\dfrac{\left(\dfrac{7}{8}\right)}{\left(-\dfrac{3}{4}\right)} = \dfrac{7}{8} \div \left(-\dfrac{3}{4}\right)$

$\qquad = \dfrac{7}{8} \cdot \left(-\dfrac{4}{3}\right)$

$\qquad = \dfrac{7 \cdot -\cancel{4}^{\,1}}{_2\cancel{8} \cdot 3}$

$\qquad = -\dfrac{7}{6}$

$\qquad = -1\dfrac{1}{6}$

29. $\dfrac{\left(-\dfrac{4}{5}\right)}{\left(-\dfrac{7}{20}\right)} = -\dfrac{4}{5} \div \left(-\dfrac{7}{20}\right)$

$\qquad = -\dfrac{4}{5} \cdot \left(-\dfrac{20}{7}\right)$

$\qquad = \dfrac{4 \cdot \cancel{20}^{\,4}}{_1\cancel{5} \cdot 7}$

$\qquad = \dfrac{4 \cdot 4}{1 \cdot 7}$

$\qquad = \dfrac{16}{7}$

$\qquad = 2\dfrac{2}{7}$

30. $\dfrac{\left(-2\dfrac{2}{5}\right)}{\left(1\dfrac{1}{5}\right)} = -\dfrac{12}{5} \div \dfrac{6}{5}$

$\qquad = \dfrac{-12}{5} \cdot \dfrac{5}{6}$

$\qquad = \dfrac{^{-2}\cancel{12} \cdot \cancel{5}^{\,1}}{_1\cancel{5} \cdot \cancel{6}_1}$

$\qquad = -2$

31. Amount of rice used on Monday − Amount of rice used on Tuesday:

$8\dfrac{5}{6} - 5\dfrac{1}{6} = \dfrac{53}{6} - \dfrac{31}{6}$

$\qquad = \dfrac{53 - 31}{6}$

$$= \frac{22}{6}$$

$$= 3\frac{2}{3} \text{ lb}$$

$3\frac{2}{3}$ pounds more rice was used on Monday than on Tuesday.

32. Number of complete lengths she can cut:

$$9\frac{2}{3} \div \frac{1}{3} = \frac{29}{3} \cdot \frac{3}{1}$$

$$= 29$$

She can cut 29 complete lengths.

33. Number of cups:

$$2\frac{1}{2} - \frac{5}{6} = \frac{5}{2} - \frac{5}{6}$$

$$= \frac{5 \cdot 3}{2 \cdot 3} - \frac{5}{6}$$

$$= \frac{15}{6} - \frac{5}{6}$$

$$= \frac{15 - 5}{6}$$

$$= \frac{10}{6}$$

$$= 1\frac{2}{3} \text{ c}$$

The chef needs $1\frac{2}{3}$ more cups of walnuts.

34. The other number:

$$-8\frac{1}{4} - \left(-5\frac{2}{3}\right) = \frac{-33}{4} + \frac{17}{3}$$

$$= \frac{-33 \cdot 3}{4 \cdot 3} + \frac{17 \cdot 4}{3 \cdot 4}$$

$$= \frac{-99}{12} + \frac{68}{12}$$

$$= \frac{-99 + 68}{12}$$

$$= \frac{-31}{12}$$

$$= -2\frac{7}{12}$$

The other number is $-2\frac{7}{12}$.

35. Total weight $= 4\frac{1}{2} + 3\frac{2}{5} + 6\frac{4}{5}$

$$= \frac{9}{2} + \frac{17}{5} + \frac{34}{5}$$

$$= \frac{9 \cdot 5}{2 \cdot 5} + \frac{17 \cdot 2}{5 \cdot 2} + \frac{34 \cdot 2}{5 \cdot 2}$$

$$= \frac{45}{10} + \frac{34}{10} + \frac{68}{10}$$

$$= \frac{45 + 34 + 68}{10}$$

$$= \frac{147}{10} \text{ lb}$$

Average weight $= \frac{147}{10} \div 3$

$$= \frac{147}{10} \cdot \frac{1}{3}$$

$$= \frac{^{49}\cancel{147} \cdot 1}{10 \cdot \cancel{3}_1}$$

$$= \frac{49}{10}$$

$$= 4\frac{9}{10} \text{ lb}$$

The average weight of the three parcels is $4\frac{9}{10}$ pounds.

Lesson 2.6

1. $|7.9| - |-3.15| = 7.9 - 3.15$
$$= 4.75$$
The sum is positive, because 7.9 has a greater absolute value.
$-3.15 + 7.9 = 4.75$

2. $|-5.3| - |0.072| = 5.3 - 0.072$
$$= 5.228$$
Use a negative sign, because -5.3 has a greater absolute value.
$0.072 + (-5.3) = -5.228$

3. $|-41.36| + |-8.2| = 41.36 + 8.2$
$$= 49.56$$
Use the common sign, a negative sign, for the sum.
$-41.36 + (-8.2) = -49.56$

4. $8.22 - (-0.355) = 8.22 + 0.355$
$$= 8.575$$

5. $|-17.203| + |-0.86| = 17.203 + 0.86$
$$= 18.063$$
Use the common sign, a negative sign, for the sum.
$-17.203 - 0.86 = -18.063$

6. $-29.5 - (-9.34) = -29.5 + 9.34$
$|-29.5| - |9.34| = 29.5 - 9.34$
$$= 20.16$$
Use a negative sign, because 29.5 has a greater absolute value.
$-29.5 - (-9.34) = -20.16$

7. $0.4 \cdot (-5.7) = -2.28$

8. $-2.7 \cdot 3.1 = -8.37$

9. $-4.36 \cdot (-1.8) = 7.848$

10. $3.04 \cdot (-6.3) = -19.152$

11. $-36.9 \div 4.5 = -8.2$

12. $159.12 \div (-3.4) = -46.8$

13. $-49.14 \div (-6.3) = 7.8$

14. $12.376 \div 0.52 = 23.8$

15. $-0.48 + (-0.1) + (-2.3)$
$= -0.58 + (-2.3)$
$= -2.88$

16. $-3.59 + 16.7 + (-150.06)$
$= 13.11 + (-150.06)$
$= -136.95$

17. $49.03 + (-7.8) - (-21.05)$
$= 49.03 - 7.8 + 21.05$
$= 49.03 + 21.05 - 7.8$
$= 70.08 - 7.8$
$= 62.28$

18. $601.03 - 467.9 + (-8.12)$
$= 133.13 - 8.12$
$= 125.01$

19. $21.4 - 6.2 + 4.2 \cdot 0.3 - 2.6$
$= 21.4 - 6.2 + 1.26 - 2.6$
$= 15.2 + 1.26 - 2.6$
$= 16.46 - 2.6$
$= 13.86$

20. $(39.3 + 6) \div 3 + 0.8 \cdot 4$
$= 45.3 \div 3 + 0.8 \cdot 4$
$= 15.1 + 0.8 \cdot 4$
$= 15.1 + 3.2$
$= 18.3$

21. Her balance
$= \$315.12 - \text{Withdrawals} + \text{Deposits}$
$= \$315.12 - \$78.95 - \$143.80 + \$63.79$
$= \$236.17 - \$143.80 + \$63.79$
$= \$92.37 + \$63.79$
$= \$156.16$
After the deposit, her balance is \$156.16.

22. George's balance:
$= \$1.55 + \$120.83 - \$78.32$
$= \$122.38 - \$78.32$
$= \$44.06$

Date	Deposit	Withdrawal	Balance
February 18	\$120.83	\$78.32	\$44.06

The balance in George's account on February 18 is \$44.06.

23. $118.4 - 191 = -72.6°F$
The lowest temperature recorded was $-72.6°F$.

24. Difference
$= \$10,400,000 - (-\$23,800,000)$
$= \$34,200,000$
The company earned \$34,200,000 more in 2011 than in 2010.

25. Total fees $= \$2.50 + \$6.75 + \$2.80$
$= \$12.05$
$\$12.05 - \$10 = \$2.05$
She needs \$2.05 more.

26. Difference in temperature
$=$ Temperature in July $-$ Temperature in January
$= 62.4 - (-9.7)$
$= 62.4 + 9.7$
$= 72.1°F$
Fairbanks is 72.1°F colder in January than in July.

27. Cost price of a hat $= \$76.50 \div 6$
$= \$12.75$
40% Profit $= 0.4 \cdot \$12.75$
$= \$5.10$
Selling Price $=$ Cost Price $+$ Profit
$= \$12.75 + \$5.10$
$= \$17.85$
The selling price of each hat should be \$17.85.

28. Original Price $= \$155.80$
20% discount $= 0.2 \cdot \$155.80$
$= \$31.16$
Discount price $= \$155.80 - \$31.16$
$= \$124.64$
The discount price is \$124.64.

29. Average temperature
$= \dfrac{\text{Sum of temperatures}}{5}$
$= \dfrac{-5.2 + (-6.7) + (-9.1) + (-10.3) + (-8.6)}{5}$
$= \dfrac{-39.9}{5}$
$= -7.98°C$
The average temperature for these 5 days is $-7.98°C$.

30. Total cost of the book:
$\$26.50 + 6\%$ Sales tax
$= \$26.50 + 0.06 \cdot \$26.50$
$= \$26.50 + \$1.59$
$= \$28.09$
Total cost of the bag:
$\$19.50 + 6\%$ sales tax
$= \$19.50 + 0.06 \cdot \$19.50$
$= \$19.50 + \$1.17$
$= \$20.67$
Total cost $= \$28.09 + \$20.67$
$= \$48.76$
Amount she has left $= \$50 - \$48.76$
$= \$1.24$
She has \$1.24 left.

Brain@Work

1. Work backward

$0 + (-73) - 55 - (-77) + 68 - (-57) + (-85)$

$= -73 - 55 + 77 + 68 + 57 - 85$

$= -128 + 77 + 68 + 57 - 85$

$= -51 + 68 + 57 - 85$

$= 17 + 57 - 85$

$= 74 - 85$

$= -11$

Check:

$-11 - (-85) + (-57) - 68 + (-77) + 55 -$
(-73)

$= -11 + 85 - 57 - 68 - 77 + 55 + 73$

$= 74 - 57 - 68 - 77 + 55 + 73$

$= 17 - 68 - 77 + 55 + 73$

$= -51 - 77 + 55 + 73$

$= -128 + 55 + 73$

$= -73 + 73$

$= 0$

2. a) $-20 + 4 \cdot (2 + 7) - 35 = -19$
  b) $-15 - 30 \div (10 - 15) = -9$
  c) $[-(-5) + 4] \cdot (2 - 7) = -45$
  d) $(9 - 15) \cdot (2 - 4) = 12$

3. $-24 \cdot 36 \cdot 2 = -1{,}728$

$-1{,}728 \div 144 \div 1 = -12$

$-1{,}728 \div -24 \div 1 = 72$

$-1{,}728 \div 2 \div 144 = -864 \div 144$

$\qquad\qquad\qquad\qquad = -6$

-24	36	2
1	-12	144
72	4	-6

Cumulative Practice for Chapters 1 and 2

1. $\dfrac{13}{4} = 3\dfrac{1}{4}$

$\qquad = 3.25$

$$
\begin{array}{r}
3.25 \\
4\overline{)13.00} \\
\underline{12} \\
10 \\
\underline{8} \\
20 \\
\underline{20} \\
0
\end{array}
$$

2. $-\dfrac{5}{11} = -0.\overline{45}$

$$
\begin{array}{r}
0.4545 \\
11\overline{)5.0000} \\
\underline{44} \\
60 \\
\underline{55} \\
50 \\
\underline{44} \\
60 \\
\underline{55} \\
5
\end{array}
$$

3. $-\dfrac{72}{150} = -\dfrac{12}{25}$

$\qquad\quad = -0.48$

$$
\begin{array}{r}
0.48 \\
25\overline{)12.00} \\
\underline{100} \\
200 \\
\underline{200} \\
0
\end{array}
$$

4. $3\dfrac{11}{12} = 3.91\overline{6}$

$$
\begin{array}{r}
0.9166 \\
12\overline{)11.0000} \\
\underline{10\ 8} \\
20 \\
\underline{12} \\
80 \\
\underline{72} \\
80 \\
\underline{72} \\
8
\end{array}
$$

5. $2.65 = 2\dfrac{65}{100}$

$\qquad\quad = \dfrac{265}{100}$

$\qquad\quad = \dfrac{53}{20}$

6. $-7.4 = -7\dfrac{4}{10}$

$\qquad\quad = -\dfrac{74}{10}$

$\qquad\quad = -\dfrac{37}{5}$

7. $48.17 = 48\dfrac{17}{100}$

$\qquad\quad = \dfrac{4{,}817}{100}$

8. $-0.225 = -\dfrac{225}{1{,}000}$

$\qquad\qquad = -\dfrac{9}{40}$

9. $\sqrt{13} \approx 3.61$

10. $-\sqrt{980} \approx -31.30$

11. $-\sqrt[3]{3{,}401} \approx -15.04$

12. $\dfrac{\pi^2}{5}$

$= \dfrac{3.1415^2}{5}$

$= \dfrac{9.8696}{5}$

≈ 1.97

13. $\sqrt{45} = 6.708...$

$\qquad\quad \approx 6.71$

14. $-\sqrt{12} = -3.464...$

$\qquad\quad \approx -3.46$

15. $\sqrt[3]{-769} = -9.161...$

$\qquad\qquad \approx -9.16$

16. $-34.2, \sqrt{79}, -\dfrac{156}{15}, 8.6\overline{57}, -\pi^3$

Rewrite as decimals.

$-34.2, 8.888, -10.4, 8.6\overline{57}, -31.006$

Arrange in ascending order.

$-34.2, -31.006, -10.4, 8.6\overline{57}, 8.888$

$-34.2, < -\pi^3 < -\dfrac{156}{15} < 8.6\overline{57} < \sqrt{79}$

17. $45{,}908 \approx 46{,}000$

18. $\sqrt{63} = 7.937\ldots$
≈ 7.94

19. $12 - (-4)$
$= 12 + 4$
$= 16$

20. $25 - (-16)$
$= 25 + 16$
$= 41$

21. $|8| = 8$
$|-10| = 10$
$|-10| - |8| = 10 - 8$
$= 2$
So, $8 + (-10) = -2$.

22. $|-11| = 11$
$|-28| = 28$
$|-11| + |-28| = 11 + 28$
$= 39$
So, $-11 + (-28) = -39$.

23. $|3| = 3$
$|-8| = 8$
$|-8| - |3| = 8 - 3$
$= 5$
So, $3 + (-8) = -5$.
$|-5| = 5$
$|7| = 7$
$|7| - |5| = 7 - 5$
$= 2$
So, $(-5) + 7 = 2$.
So, $3 + (-8) + 7 = 2$.

24. $|-6| = 6$
$|8| = 8$
$|8| - |-6| = 8 - 6$
$= 2$
So, $-6 + 8 = 2$.
$|-5| = 5$
$|2| = 2$
$|-5| - |2| = 5 - 2$
$= 3$
So, $2 + (-5) = -3$.
So, $-6 + 8 - 5 = -3$.

25. $-5 - 3 = -5 + (-3)$
$|-5| = 5$
$|-3| = 3$
$|-5| + |-3| = 5 + 3$
$= 8$
So, $-5 - 3 = -8$.

$-8 - (-4) = -8 + 4$
$|-8| = 8$
$|4| = 4$
$|-8| - |4| = 8 - 4$
$= 4$
So, $-8 - (-4) = -4$.
So, $-5 - 3 - (-4) = -4$.

26. $|-350| = 350$
$|420| = 420$
$|420| - |350| = 420 - 350$
$= 70$
So, $-350 + 420 = 70$.

27. $-108 - (-113)$
$= -108 + 113$
$|-108| = 108$
$|113| = 113$
$|113| - |-108| = 113 - 108$
$= 5$
So, $-108 - (-113) = 5$.

28. $|33| = 33$
$|-85| = 85$
$|-85| - |33| = 85 - 33$
$= 52$
So, $33 + (-85) = -52$.
$-52 - (-12) = -52 + 12$
$|-52| = 52$
$|12| = 12$
$|-52| - |12| = 52 - 12$
$= 40$
So, $-52 - (-12) = -40$.
So, $33 + (-85) - (-12) = -40$.

29. $-14 \cdot 6 = -84$

30. $-99 \div (-9) = \dfrac{-99}{-9}$
$= 11$

31. $\dfrac{5}{16} \cdot \left(-\dfrac{8}{15}\right) = \dfrac{\overset{1}{\cancel{5}} \cdot -8}{_2\cancel{16} \cdot {}_3\cancel{15}}$
$= -\dfrac{1}{6}$

32. $-\dfrac{3}{8} \div \left(-\dfrac{27}{6}\right) = -\dfrac{3}{8} \cdot \left(-\dfrac{6}{27}\right)$

$= \dfrac{\overset{1}{\cancel{3}} \cdot \cancel{6}^{\,\overset{1}{\cancel{3}}}}{_4\cancel{8} \cdot \cancel{27}\,_{{}_3}}$

$= \dfrac{1}{12}$

33. $1\frac{5}{11} \cdot \left(-2\frac{1}{5}\right)$

$= \frac{16}{11} \cdot -\frac{11}{5}$

$= \frac{16 \cdot -\cancel{11}^{1}}{_{1}\cancel{11} \cdot 5}$

$= -\frac{16}{5}$

$= -3\frac{1}{5}$

34. $\dfrac{\left(-\dfrac{2}{3}\right)}{\left(3\dfrac{1}{6}\right)}$

$= \dfrac{\left(-\dfrac{2}{3}\right)}{\left(\dfrac{19}{6}\right)}$

$= -\frac{2}{3} \div \frac{19}{6}$

$= -\frac{2}{3} \cdot \frac{6}{19}$

$= \frac{-2 \cdot \cancel{6}^{2}}{_{1}\cancel{3} \cdot 19}$

$= -\frac{4}{19}$

35. $-4[10 - (-7)] + [(-9) + 3(-4)] \div 7$

$= -4 \cdot (10 + 7) + (-9 - 12) \div 7$

$= -4 \cdot 17 + (-21) \div 7$

$= -68 - 3$

$= -71$

36. $\frac{3}{5}\left(\frac{1}{3} - \frac{5}{6}\right) + 1\frac{4}{15} + 2\left(-\frac{9}{20}\right)$

$= \frac{3}{5}\left(\frac{1}{3} - \frac{5}{6}\right) + \frac{19}{15} + 2\left(-\frac{9}{20}\right)$

$= \frac{3}{5}\left(\frac{2}{6} - \frac{5}{6}\right) + \frac{19}{15} + 2\left(-\frac{9}{20}\right)$

$= \frac{3}{5}\left(-\frac{3}{6}\right) + \frac{19}{15} + 2\left(-\frac{9}{20}\right)$

$= \frac{3}{5}\left(-\frac{1}{2}\right) + \frac{19}{15} + \left(-\frac{9}{10}\right)$

$= -\frac{3}{10} + \frac{19}{15} - \frac{9}{10}$

$= -\frac{9}{30} + \frac{38}{30} - \frac{27}{30}$

$= \frac{-9 + 38 - 27}{30}$

$= \frac{-36 + 38}{30}$

$= \frac{2}{30}$

$= \frac{1}{15}$

37. $-3[4.1 - (-2.3)] - 0.4[-6.7 + 3(2.4)]$

$= -3[4.1 - (-2.3)] + (-0.4)[-6.7 + 3(2.4)]$

$= -3 \cdot (4.1 + 2.3) + (-0.4)(-6.7 + 7.2)$

$= -3 \cdot 6.4 + (-0.4) \cdot 0.5$

$= -19.2 - 0.2$

$= -19.4$

38. $-\frac{1}{4}[-18 + 2.4(-3.5 + 2.5)] + 2\frac{1}{4} + (-8.4)$

$= -\frac{1}{4}[-18 + 2.4(-1)] + 2.25 + (-8.4)$

$= -\frac{1}{4}(-18 - 2.4) + 2.25 + (-8.4)$

$= -\frac{1}{4}(-20.4) + 2.25 + (-8.4)$

$= 5.1 + 2.25 - 8.4$

$= -1.05$

39. $\dfrac{-\dfrac{5}{6} + 1\dfrac{1}{3}}{3\left[\dfrac{1}{6} - \left(-\dfrac{4}{9}\right)\right]}$

$= \dfrac{-\dfrac{5}{6} + \dfrac{4}{3}}{3\left[\dfrac{1}{6} - \left(-\dfrac{4}{9}\right)\right]}$

$= \dfrac{-\dfrac{5}{6} + \dfrac{8}{6}}{3\left[\dfrac{1}{6} - \left(-\dfrac{4}{9}\right)\right]}$

$= \dfrac{\dfrac{-5 + 8}{6}}{3\left[\dfrac{1}{6} - \left(-\dfrac{4}{9}\right)\right]}$

$= \dfrac{\dfrac{3}{6}}{3\left[\dfrac{1}{6} + \dfrac{4}{9}\right]}$

$= \dfrac{\dfrac{1}{2}}{3\left(\dfrac{3}{18} + \dfrac{8}{18}\right)}$

$= \dfrac{\dfrac{1}{2}}{3\left(\dfrac{3 + 8}{18}\right)}$

$= \dfrac{\dfrac{1}{2}}{3\left(\dfrac{11}{18}\right)}$

$= \dfrac{\dfrac{1}{2}}{\left(\dfrac{11}{6}\right)}$

$= \frac{1}{2} \cdot \frac{6}{11}$

$= \frac{1}{_{1}\cancel{2}} \cdot \frac{\cancel{6}^{3}}{11}$

$= \frac{3}{11}$

40. Circumference $= 2\pi r$

$$83.5 \approx 2 \cdot 3.14 \cdot r$$
$$83.5 \approx 6.28 \cdot r$$
$$\frac{83.5}{6.28} \approx \frac{6.28r}{6.28}$$
$$13.2961 \approx r$$
$$13.3 \text{ cm} \approx r$$

The radius of the circle is about 13.3 cm.

41. Average $= \dfrac{\text{Sum of speed of 4 cars}}{4}$

$$= \frac{146.633 + 150 + 151.971 + 141.428}{4}$$

$$= \frac{590.032}{4}$$

$$= 147.508$$

$$\approx 147.51 \text{ mi/h}$$

The average speed of the 4 cars is about 147.51 miles per hour.

42. Diver's new depth:
$-62 - 39 + 48 = -53$ ft
The diver's new depth is 53 feet below sea level.

43. Total number of yards after the third down:
$$15 - 12 - 6 = 15 - 18$$
$$= -3 \text{ yd}$$
Let x be the number of yards the football team needs to gain on the fourth down.
$$-3 + x = 10$$
$$-3 + x + 3 = 10 + 3$$
$$x = 13 \text{ yd}$$
The team needs to gain 13 yards from their starting position.

44. Difference in height:
$$864 - (-68) = 864 + 68$$
$$= 932 \text{ ft}$$
The difference in height between the top of the hill and the shifting rock is 932 feet.

45. Total score:
$$8(5) + 6(3) + 12(-2) + 4(-4)$$
$$= 40 + 18 - 24 - 16$$
$$= 18$$
Jason's score for the survey is 18 points.

46. Range of temperature:
$$116.1 - (-14.3) = 116.1 + 14.3$$
$$= 130.4°F$$
The range of temperatures in Bolivia is 130.4°F.

47. Total length of two planks:

$$4\frac{1}{4} + 2\frac{1}{2} = \frac{17}{4} + \frac{5}{2}$$
$$= \frac{17}{4} + \frac{5 \cdot 2}{2 \cdot 2}$$
$$= \frac{17}{4} + \frac{10}{4}$$
$$= \frac{17 + 10}{4}$$
$$= \frac{27}{4} \text{ ft}$$

Length of new plank:

$$\frac{27}{4} - 2 \cdot \frac{5}{12} = \frac{27}{4} - \frac{10}{12}$$
$$= \frac{27 \cdot 3}{4 \cdot 3} - \frac{10}{12}$$
$$= \frac{81}{12} - \frac{10}{12}$$
$$= \frac{81 - 10}{12}$$
$$= \frac{71}{12}$$
$$= 5\frac{11}{2} \text{ ft}$$

The length of the new plank is $= 5\frac{11}{2}$ feet.

48. Difference in height:
$$2,150 - 1,430 = 720 \text{ ft}$$
$$\text{Change in height} = \frac{720}{4}$$
$$= 180 \text{ ft/min}$$

The average change in balloon height is 180 feet per minute.

Chapter 3

Lesson 3.1

1. $0.8x + 0.5x = 1.3x$

2. $0.1y + 0.9y = 1y$
$\qquad\qquad\quad = y$

3. $1.4p + 0.3p = 1.7p$

4. $0.8m + 2.7m = 3.5m$

5. $2.3a + 0.8a = 3.1a$

6. $1.1b + 2.8b = 3.9b$

7. $\dfrac{1}{7}p + \dfrac{5}{7}p = \dfrac{6}{7}p$

8. $\frac{3}{5}a + \frac{2}{5}a = \frac{5}{5}a$

$\qquad = 1a$

$\qquad = a$

9. $\frac{4}{9}m + \frac{2}{9}m = \frac{6}{9}m$

$\qquad = \frac{2}{3}m$

10. $\frac{5}{8}b + \frac{1}{8}b = \frac{6}{8}b$

$\qquad = \frac{3}{4}b$

11. $\frac{4}{7}x + \frac{5}{14}x = \frac{8}{14}x + \frac{5}{14}x$

$\qquad = \frac{13}{14}x$

12. $\frac{2}{5}y + \frac{3}{10}y = \frac{4}{10}y + \frac{3}{10}y$

$\qquad = \frac{7}{10}y$

13. $\frac{3}{8}p + \frac{3}{16}p = \frac{6}{16}p + \frac{3}{16}p$

$\qquad = \frac{9}{16}p$

14. $\frac{2}{9}m + \frac{2}{3}m = \frac{2}{9}m + \frac{6}{9}m$

$\qquad = \frac{8}{9}m$

15. $\frac{2}{3}x + \frac{1}{4}x = \frac{8}{12}x + \frac{3}{12}x$

$\qquad = \frac{11}{12}x$

16. $\frac{5}{12}y + \frac{3}{4}y = \frac{5}{12}y + \frac{9}{12}y$

$\qquad = \frac{14}{12}y$

$\qquad = \frac{7}{6}y$

17. a) Perimeter of triangle A:

$\frac{1}{3}x + \frac{2}{3}x + \frac{1}{6}x = \frac{2}{6}x + \frac{4}{6}x + \frac{1}{6}x$

$\qquad\qquad = \frac{7}{6}x$ units

The perimeter of triangle A is $\frac{7}{6}x$ units.

b) Perimeter of triangle B:

$\frac{4}{9}x + \frac{4}{9}x + \frac{4}{9}x = \frac{12}{9}x$

$\qquad\qquad = \frac{4}{3}x$ units

The perimeter of triangle B is $\frac{4}{3}x$ units.

c) Sum of the perimeters of the two triangles: $\frac{7}{6}x + \frac{4}{3}x = \frac{7}{6}x + \frac{8}{6}x$

$\qquad\qquad = \frac{15}{6}x$

$\qquad\qquad = \frac{5}{2}x$

The sum of the perimeters of the two triangles is $\frac{5}{2}x$ units.

18. Sum of the areas of the two cards:
$5.3 \cdot 2x + 4 \cdot 1.6x = 10.6x + 6.4x$

$\qquad\qquad = 17x$ in^2

The sum of the areas of the two cards is $17x$ square inches.

Lesson 3.2

1. $1.7x - 0.5x = 1.2x$

2. $1.9y - 1.6y = 0.3y$

3. $2.4p - 1.8p = 0.6p$

4. $3.8q - 2.5q = 1.3q$

5. $3.2a - 2.9a = 0.3a$

6. $1.3b - 0.9b = 0.4b$

7. $\frac{7}{9}x - \frac{4}{9}x = \frac{3}{9}x$

$\qquad = \frac{1}{3}x$

8. $\frac{6}{7}y - \frac{2}{7}y = \frac{4}{7}y$

9. $\frac{9}{10}p - \frac{7}{10}p = \frac{2}{10}p$

$\qquad = \frac{1}{5}p$

10. $\frac{5}{8}m - \frac{3}{8}m = \frac{2}{8}m$

$\qquad = \frac{1}{4}m$

11. $\frac{4}{5}y - \frac{1}{3}y = \frac{12}{15}y - \frac{5}{15}y$

$\qquad = \frac{7}{15}y$

12. $\frac{5}{6}x - \frac{4}{5}x = \frac{25}{30}x - \frac{24}{30}x$

$\qquad = \frac{1}{30}x$

13. $\frac{7}{9}p - \frac{1}{3}p = \frac{7}{9}p - \frac{3}{9}p$

$\qquad = \frac{4}{9}p$

14. $\frac{10}{3}m - \frac{7}{4}m = \frac{40}{12}m - \frac{21}{12}m$

$\qquad = \frac{19}{12}m$

15. $\frac{9}{7}a - \frac{1}{3}a = \frac{27}{21}a - \frac{7}{21}a$

$\qquad = \frac{20}{21}a$

16. $\frac{7}{10}b - \frac{2}{5}b = \frac{7}{10}b - \frac{4}{10}b$

$\qquad = \frac{3}{10}b$

17. Difference in length: $15.3y - 12.8y = 2.5y$ in.
The difference in the length of the two ropes is 2.5y inches.

18. Area of the shaded border: $12.2y \cdot 7 - 10.5y \cdot 5$

$\qquad = 85.4y - 52.5y$

$\qquad = 32.9y$ in^2

The area of the shaded border is 32.9y square inches.

Lesson 3.3

1. $2.1x + 0.8x - 3 = 2.9x - 3$

2. $1.6y + 1.9y + 1.3 = 3.5y + 1.3$

3. $3.5p - 2.8p - 1 = 0.7p - 1$

4. $4.2q - 3.7q - 5 = 0.5q - 5$

5. $\frac{5}{9}a + \frac{4}{9}a + \frac{5}{9} = \frac{9}{9}a + \frac{5}{9}$

$\qquad = 1a + \frac{5}{9}$

$\qquad = a + \frac{5}{9}$

6. $\frac{7}{8}b + \frac{1}{4}b - 3 = \frac{7}{8}b + \frac{2}{8}b - 3$

$\qquad = \frac{9}{8}b - 3$

7. $\frac{9}{2}m - \frac{1}{3}m + 7 = \frac{27}{6}m - \frac{2}{6}m + 7$

$\qquad = \frac{25}{6}m + 7$

8. $\frac{8}{3}n - \frac{8}{9}n - 3 = \frac{24}{9}n - \frac{8}{9}n - 3$

$\qquad = \frac{16}{9}n - 3$

9. $1.5x + 0.8x + 0.6x = 2.9x$

10. $3.2y + 4.7y + 0.6y = 8.5y$

11. $5.4a - 2.7a - 0.8a = 1.9a$

12. $4.8b + 1.2b - 3.9b = 2.1b$

13. $\frac{1}{7}p + \frac{4}{7}p + \frac{1}{7}p = \frac{6}{7}p$

14. $\frac{7}{9}q + \frac{1}{3}q + \frac{1}{9}q = \frac{7}{9}q + \frac{3}{9}q + \frac{1}{9}q$

$\qquad = \frac{11}{9}q$

15. $\frac{3}{4}m + \frac{2}{3}m - \frac{1}{6}m = \frac{9}{12}m + \frac{8}{12}m - \frac{2}{12}m$

$\qquad = \frac{15}{12}m$

$\qquad = \frac{5}{4}m$

16. $\frac{7}{8}n + \frac{3}{4}n - \frac{1}{2}n = \frac{7}{8}n + \frac{6}{8}n - \frac{4}{8}n$

$\qquad = \frac{9}{8}n$

17. $4x + 9 + 8x = (4x + 8x) + 9$

$\qquad = 12x + 9$

18. $5y + 3 + 11y = (5y + 11y) + 3$

$\qquad = 16y + 3$

19. $7a - 5 - 3a = (7a - 3a) - 5$

$\qquad = 4a - 5$

20. $16b - 9 + 5b = (16b + 5b) - 9$

$\qquad = 21b - 9$

21. $1.1p + 2.3 - 0.5p = (1.1p - 0.5p) + 2.3$

$\qquad = 0.6p + 2.3$

22. $6.3q - 1.8 - 5.7q = (6.3q - 5.7q) - 1.8$

$\qquad = 0.6q - 1.8$

23. $\frac{3}{5}m + \frac{2}{3} + \frac{7}{10}m = \left(\frac{3}{5}m + \frac{7}{10}m\right) + \frac{2}{3}$

$\qquad = \left(\frac{6}{10}m + \frac{7}{10}m\right) + \frac{2}{3}$

$\qquad = \frac{13}{10}m + \frac{2}{3}$

24. $\frac{5}{6}n - \frac{2}{3} - \frac{1}{2}n = \left(\frac{5}{6}n - \frac{1}{2}n\right) - \frac{2}{3}$

$\qquad = \left(\frac{5}{6}n - \frac{3}{6}n\right) - \frac{2}{3}$

$\qquad = \frac{2}{6}n - \frac{2}{3}$

$\qquad = \frac{1}{3}n - \frac{2}{3}$

25. $5x + x + 5y = 6x + 5y$

26. $13x + 9x + 4y = 22x + 4y$

27. $15p - 8p + 6q = 7p + 6q$

28. $24m - 16m + 5n = 8m + 5n$

29. $11a + 3a + 5b - b = 14a + 4b$

30. $9b - 2a + 3b - a = (9b + 3b) + (-2a - a)$

$\qquad = 12b - 3a$

31. $2.7m + 0.5m + 3.2n + 0.8n = 3.2m + 4n$

32. $18.5p - 16.6p - 4.3q + 2.7q = 1.9p - 1.6q$

33. $\frac{3}{7}x + \frac{1}{7}x - \frac{1}{6}y + \frac{5}{6}y = \frac{4}{7}x + \frac{4}{6}y$

$$= \frac{4}{7}x + \frac{2}{3}y$$

34. $\frac{3}{4}p - \frac{1}{2}p + \frac{5}{9}q - \frac{1}{3}q = \frac{3}{4}p - \frac{2}{4}p + \frac{5}{9}q - \frac{3}{9}q$

$$= \frac{1}{4}p + \frac{2}{9}q$$

35. $6.4m + 2.3n - 5.7m - 0.7n$

$= (6.4m - 5.7m) + (2.3n - 0.7n)$

$= 0.7m + 1.6n$

36. $6.9a - 4.9b - 7.8a - 0.4b$

$= (6.9a - 7.8a) + (-4.9b - 0.4b)$

$= -0.9a - 5.3b$

37. $\frac{8}{9}x - \frac{4}{5}y - \frac{2}{3}x - \frac{1}{2}y$

$= \left(\frac{8}{9}x - \frac{2}{3}x\right) + \left(-\frac{4}{5}y - \frac{1}{2}y\right)$

$= \left(\frac{8}{9}x - \frac{6}{9}x\right) + \left(-\frac{8}{10}y - \frac{5}{10}y\right)$

$= \frac{2}{9}x + \left(-\frac{13}{10}y\right)$

$= \frac{2}{9}x - \frac{13}{10}y$

38. $\frac{8}{5}a - \frac{7}{4}b - \frac{2}{3}a + \frac{5}{8}b$

$= \left(\frac{8}{5}a - \frac{2}{3}a\right) + \left(-\frac{7}{4}b + \frac{5}{8}b\right)$

$= \frac{24}{15}a - \frac{10}{15}a + \left(-\frac{14}{8}b + \frac{5}{8}b\right)$

$= \frac{14}{15}a + \left(-\frac{9}{8}b\right)$

$= \frac{14}{15}a - \frac{9}{8}b$

39. Perimeter $= 2 \cdot 4.6x + 2 \cdot 2.8x$

$= 9.2x + 5.6x$

$= 14.8x$ units

40. Perimeter $= 2x + \frac{3}{2}x + \frac{5}{2}x$

$= 6x$ units

Lesson 3.4

1. $\frac{1}{4}(8x + 16) = \frac{1}{4}(8x) + \frac{1}{4}(16)$

$= 2x + 4$

2. $\frac{1}{3}(3p + 12) = \frac{1}{3}(3p) + \frac{1}{3}(12)$

$= p + 4$

3. $\frac{1}{2}(14k - 10) = \frac{1}{2}[14k + (-10)]$

$= \frac{1}{2}(14k) + \frac{1}{2}(-10)$

$= 7k + (-5)$

$= 7k - 5$

4. $\frac{1}{8}(8a - 24) = \frac{1}{8}[8a + (-24)]$

$= \frac{1}{8}(8a) + \frac{1}{8}(-24)$

$= a + (-3)$

$= a - 3$

5. $\frac{1}{2}(4p + 1) = \frac{1}{2}(4p) + \frac{1}{2}(1)$

$= 2p + \frac{1}{2}$

6. $\frac{1}{7}(2a + 5) = \frac{1}{7}(2a) + \frac{1}{7}(5)$

$= \frac{2}{7}a + \frac{5}{7}$

7. $\frac{1}{5}(3b - 2) = \frac{1}{5}[3b + (-2)]$

$= \frac{1}{5}(3b) + \frac{1}{5}(-2)$

$= \frac{3}{5}b + \left(-\frac{2}{5}\right)$

$= \frac{3}{5}b - \frac{2}{5}$

8. $\frac{3}{5}(2k - 15) = \frac{3}{5}[2k + (-15)]$

$= \frac{3}{5}(2k) + \frac{3}{5}(-15)$

$= \frac{6}{5}k + (-9)$

$= \frac{6}{5}k - 9$

9. $2(6x + 0.1) = 2(6x) + 2(0.1)$

$= 12x + 0.2$

10. $5(0.3y + 2) = 5(0.3y) + 5(2)$

$= 1.5y + 10$

11. $0.3(5x + 3) = 0.3(5x) + 0.3(3)$

$= 1.5x + 0.9$

12. $0.4(2h + 7) = 0.4(2h) + 0.4(7)$

$= 0.8h + 2.8$

13. $0.6(m - 4) = 0.6[m + (-4)]$

$= 0.6(m) + 0.6(-4)$

$= 0.6m + (-2.4)$

$= 0.6m - 2.4$

14. $0.5(p - 3) = 0.5[p + (-3)]$

$= 0.5(p) + 0.5(-3)$

$= 0.5p + (-1.5)$

$= 0.5p - 1.5$

15. $0.2(1.2d + 0.3) = 0.2(1.2d) + 0.2(0.3)$
$$= 0.24d + 0.06$$

16. $1.5(0.4x - 1.3) = 1.5[0.4x + (-1.3)]$
$$= 1.5(0.4x) + 1.5(-1.3)$$
$$= 0.6x + (-1.95)$$
$$= 0.6x - 1.95$$

17. $-3(x + 2) = -3(x) + (-3)(2)$
$$= -3x + (-6)$$
$$= -3x - 6$$

18. $-5(2x + 3) = -5(2x) + (-5)(3)$
$$= -10x + (-15)$$
$$= -10x - 15$$

19. $-2(3a + 7b) = -2(3a) + (-2)(7b)$
$$= -6a + (-14b)$$
$$= -6a - 14b$$

20. $-7(4k - h) = -7(4k) + (-7)(-h)$
$$= -28k + 7h$$

21. $-6\left(\frac{1}{2}p + 3\right) = -6\left(\frac{1}{2}p\right) + (-6)(3)$
$$= -3p + (-18)$$
$$= -3p - 18$$

22. $-\frac{1}{4}\left(8x - \frac{1}{3}\right) = \left(-\frac{1}{4}\right)(8x) + \left(-\frac{1}{4}\right)\left(-\frac{1}{3}\right)$
$$= -2x + \frac{1}{12}$$

23. $-3(4k + 1.2) = -3(4k) + (-3)(1.2)$
$$= -12k + (-3.6)$$
$$= -12k - 3.6$$

24. $-4(0.3m + 7) = -4(0.3m) + (-4)(7)$
$$= -1.2m + (-28)$$
$$= -1.2m - 28$$

25. $-5(q - 0.6) = -5(q) + (-5)(-0.6)$
$$= -5q + 3$$

26. $-0.2(0.6y - 2) = -0.2(0.6y) + (-0.2)(-2)$
$$= -0.12y + 0.4$$

27. $2(3y + 2) + 5 = 2(3y) + 2(2) + 5$
$$= 6y + 4 + 5$$
$$= 6y + 9$$

28. $4(3a + 1) - 2 = 4(3a) + 4(1) - 2$
$$= 12a + 4 - 2$$
$$= 12a + 2$$

29. $3(x + 8) + 5x = 3(x) + 3(8) + 5x$
$$= 3x + 24 + 5x$$
$$= (3x + 5x) + 24$$
$$= 8x + 24$$

30. $7(b + 4) - 3b = 7(b) + 7(4) - 3b$
$$= 7b + 28 - 3b$$
$$= (7b - 3b) + 28$$
$$= 4b + 28$$

31. $3\left(\frac{1}{4}a + 2\right) + 5 = 3\left(\frac{1}{4}a\right) + 3(2) + 5$
$$= \frac{3}{4}a + 6 + 5$$
$$= \frac{3}{4}a + 11$$

32. $6\left(\frac{1}{12}a - 3\right) - \frac{1}{2}a = 6\left(\frac{1}{12}a\right) + 6(-3) - \frac{1}{2}a$
$$= \frac{6}{12}a + (-18) - \frac{1}{2}a$$
$$= \left(\frac{6}{12}a - \frac{1}{2}a\right) + (-18)$$
$$= \left(\frac{1}{2}a - \frac{1}{2}a\right) + (-18)$$
$$= -18$$

33. $0.4(x + 3) + 0.8x = 0.4(x) + 0.4(3) + 0.8x$
$$= 0.4x + 1.2 + 0.8x$$
$$= (0.4x + 0.8x) + 1.2$$
$$= 1.2x + 1.2$$

34. $0.3(y + 5) - 0.1y = 0.3(y) + 0.3(5) - 0.1y$
$$= 0.3y + 1.5 - 0.1y$$
$$= (0.3y - 0.1y) + 1.5$$
$$= 0.2y + 1.5$$

35. $-3(5m + 1) - m = -3(5m) + (-3)(1) - m$
$$= -15m + (-3) - m$$
$$= (-15m - m) + (-3)$$
$$= -16m + (-3)$$
$$= -16m - 3$$

36. $12 - 4(n - 2) = 12 + (-4)(n) + (-4)(-2)$
$$= 12 + (-4n) + 8$$
$$= (12 + 8) + (-4n)$$
$$= 20 + (-4n)$$
$$= 20 - 4n$$

37. $-0.6(r + 4) + 2.5r = -0.6(r) + (-0.6)(4) + 2.5r$
$$= -0.6r + (-2.4) + 2.5r$$
$$= (-0.6r + 2.5r) + (-2.4)$$
$$= 1.9r + (-2.4)$$
$$= 1.9r - 2.4$$

38. $-(1.4x + 5) + 1.7x = (-1)(1.4x) + (-1)(5)$
$$+ 1.7x$$
$$= -1.4x + (-5) + 1.7x$$
$$= (-1.4x + 1.7x) + (-5)$$
$$= 0.3x + (-5)$$
$$= 0.3x - 5$$

39. $15y + 4(8y + x) = 15y + 4(8y) + 4(x)$
$$= 15y + 32y + 4x$$
$$= 47y + 4x$$

40. $9a + 7(2a - b) = 9a + 7(2a) + 7(-b)$
$$= 9a + 14a + (-7b)$$
$$= 23a + (-7b)$$
$$= 23a - 7b$$

41. $6g + 8(v - g) = 6g + 8(v) + 8(-g)$
$= 6g + 8v + (-8g)$
$= [6g + (-8g)] + 8v$
$= (6g - 8g) + 8v$
$= -2g + 8v$

42. $12p + 10(p - 2q) = 12p + 10(p) + 10(-2q)$
$= 12p + 10p + (-20q)$
$= 22p + (-20q)$
$= 22p - 20q$

43. $7(2a + b) + 2(3a + b)$
$= 7(2a) + 7(b) + 2(3a) + 2(b)$
$= 14a + 7b + 6a + 2b$
$= (14a + 6a) + (7b + 2b)$
$= 20a + 9b$

44. $4(2m - n) + 8(3n - m)$
$= 4(2m) + 4(-n) + 8(3n) + 8(-m)$
$= 8m + (-4n) + 24n + (-8m)$
$= [8m + (-8m)] + [(-4n) + 24n]$
$= (8m - 8m) + (-4n + 24n)$
$= 20n$

45. $5(3d + e) - 4(d - 4e)$
$= 5(3d) + 5(e) + (-4)(d) + (-4)(-4e)$
$= 15d + 5e + (-4d) + 16e$
$= [15d + (-4d)] + (5e + 16e)$
$= (15d - 4d) + (5e + 16e)$
$= 11d + 21e$

46. $6(4q - p) - (2q - 5p)$
$= 6(4q) + 6(-p) + (-1)(2q) + (-1)(-5p)$
$= 24q + (-6p) + (-2q) + 5p$
$= [24q + (-2q)] + [(-6p) + 5p]$
$= (24q - 2q) + (-6p + 5p)$
$= 22q - p$

47. $-3(x + 2y) + 4(3x - 6y)$
$= -3(x) + (-3)(2y) + 4(3x) + 4(-6y)$
$= -3x + (-6y) + 12x + (-24y)$
$= (-3x + 12x) + [(-6y) + (-24y)]$
$= (-3x + 12x) + (-6y - 24y)$
$= 9x + (-30y)$
$= 9x - 30y$

48. $-8(y + 3t) - 4(2y - t)$
$= -8(y) + (-8)(3t) + (-4)(2y) + (-4)(-t)$
$= -8y + (-24t) + (-8y) + 4t$
$= [-8y + (-8y)] + [(-24t) + 4t]$
$= (-8y - 8y) + (-24t + 4t)$
$= -16y - 20t$

49. Length of missing dimension:
$14 - (x - 3) = 14 + (-1)(x) + (-1)(-3)$
$= 14 + (-x) + 3$
$= (14 + 3) + (-x)$
$= 17 + (-x)$
$= (17 - x)$ units
Area $= 12 \cdot (17 - x)$
$= 12(17) + 12(-x)$
$= 204 + (-12x)$
$= (204 - 12x)$ units^2

50. Length of missing dimension:
$(16 - 2x)$ units
Area $= \frac{1}{2} \cdot 8 \cdot (16 - 2x)$
$= 4 \cdot (16 - 2x)$
$= 4(16) + (4)(-2x)$
$= 64 + (-8x)$
$= (64 - 8x)$ units^2

51. Area $= 10(2x - 3y) + \frac{1}{2} \cdot 10 \cdot 6y$
$= 10(2x) + 10(-3y) + 30y$
$= 10(2x) + (-30y) + 30y$
$= 20x - 30y + 30y$
$= 20x$ units^2

Lesson 3.5

1. $3x + 15 = 3(x) + 3(5)$
$= 3(x + 5)$

2. $8a + 8 = 8(a) + 8(1)$
$= 8(a + 1)$

3. $4x - 28 = 4x + (-28)$
$= 4(x) + 4(-7)$
$= 4(x - 7)$

4. $5x - 15 = 5x + (-15)$
$= 5(x) + 5(-3)$
$= 5(x - 3)$

5. $6a + 6b = 6(a) + 6(b)$
$= 6(a + b)$

6. $2x + 10y = 2(x) + 2(5y)$
$= 2(x + 5y)$

7. $21p + 7q = 7(3p) + 7(q)$
$= 7(3p + q)$

8. $16w + 80m = 16(w) + 16(5m)$
$= 16(w + 5m)$

9. $3j - 18k = 3j + (-18k)$
$= 3(j) + 3(-6k)$
$= 3(j - 6k)$

10. $12t - 48u = 12t + (-48u)$
$= 12(t) + 12(-4u)$
$= 12(t - 4u)$

11. $25a - 5p = 25a + (-5p)$
$= 5(5a) + 5(-p)$
$= 5(5a - p)$

12. $8h - 56f = 8h + (-56f)$
$= 8(h) + 8(-7f)$
$= 8(h - 7f)$

13. $16x - 10y = 16x + (-10y)$
$= 2(8x) + 2(-5y)$
$= 2(8x - 5y)$

14. $24a - 6b = 24a + (-6b)$
$= 6(4a) + 6(-b)$
$= 6(4a - b)$

15. $35c - 15d = 35c + (-15d)$
$$= 5(7c) + 5(-3d)$$
$$= 5(7c - 3d)$$

16. $14y - 30e = 14y + (-30e)$
$$= 2(7y) + 2(-15e)$$
$$= 2(7y - 15e)$$

17. $-3 - p = -3 + (-p)$
$$= (-1)(3) + (-1)(p)$$
$$= (-1)(3 + p)$$
$$= -(3 + p)$$

18. $-y - 8 = -y + (-8)$
$$= (-1)(y) + (-1)(8)$$
$$= (-1)(y + 8)$$
$$= -(y + 8)$$

19. $-4d - 5 = -4d + (-5)$
$$= (-1)(4d) + (-1)(5)$$
$$= (-1)(4d + 5)$$
$$= -(4d + 5)$$

20. $-5y - 16 = -5y + (-16)$
$$= (-1)(5y) + (-1)(16)$$
$$= (-1)(5y + 16)$$
$$= -(5y + 16)$$

21. $-2a - 4 = -2a + (-4)$
$$= (-2)(a) + (-2)(2)$$
$$= -2(a + 2)$$

22. $-3x - 24 = -3x + (-24)$
$$= (-3)(x) + (-3)(8)$$
$$= -3(x + 8)$$

23. $-7k - 35 = -7k + (-35)$
$$= (-7)(k) + (-7)(5)$$
$$= -7(k + 5)$$

24. $-9u - 81 = -9u + (-81)$
$$= (-9)(u) + (-9)(9)$$
$$= -9(u + 9)$$

25. $-2 - 6n = -2 + (-6n)$
$$= (-2)(1) + (-2)(3n)$$
$$= -2(1 + 3n)$$

26. $-4 - 12p = -4 + (-12p)$
$$= (-4)(1) + (-4)(3p)$$
$$= -4(1 + 3p)$$

27. $-24x - 18y = -24x + (-18y)$
$$= (-6)(4x) + (-6)(3y)$$
$$= -6(4x + 3y)$$

28. $-35m - 20n = -35m + (-20n)$
$$= (-5)(7m) + (-5)(4n)$$
$$= -5(7m + 4n)$$

29. $-28w - 7q = -28w + (-7q)$
$$= (-7)(4w) + (-7)(q)$$
$$= -7(4w + q)$$

30. $-48y - 16x = -48y + (-16x)$
$$= (-16)(3y) + (-16)(x)$$
$$= -16(3y + x)$$

31. $3x + 3y + 9 = 3(x) + 3(y) + 3(3)$
$$= 3(x + y + 3)$$

32. $4a + 2b + 6 = 2(2a) + 2(b) + 2(3)$
$$= 2(2a + b + 3)$$

33. $15p + 5q + 10 = 5(3p) + 5(q) + 5(2)$
$$= 5(3p + q + 2)$$

34. $18d + 9e + 12 = 3(6d) + 3(3e) + 3(4)$
$$= 3(6d + 3e + 4)$$

35. $4s - 8t - 20 = 4s + (-8t) + (-20)$
$$= 4(s) + 4(-2t) + 4(-5)$$
$$= 4[s + (-2t) + (-5)]$$
$$= 4(s - 2t - 5)$$

36. $7a - 14b - 28 = 7a + (-14b) + (-28)$
$$= 7(a) + 7(-2b) + 7(-4)$$
$$= 7[a + (-2b) + (-4)]$$
$$= 7(a - 2b - 4)$$

37. $16a - 12b - 6 = 16a + (-12b) + (-6)$
$$= 2(8a) + 2(-6b) + 2(-3)$$
$$= 2[8a + (-6b) + (-3)]$$
$$= 2(8a - 6b - 3)$$

38. $33g - 11h - 66 = 33g + (-11h) + (-66)$
$$= 11(3g) + 11(-h) + 11(-6)$$
$$= 11[3g + (-h) + (-6)]$$
$$= 11(3g - h - 6)$$

39. $9 + 18m - 12n = 9 + 18m + (-12n)$
$$= 3(3) + 3(6m) + 3(-4n)$$
$$= 3[3 + 6m + (-4n)]$$
$$= 3(3 + 6m - 4n)$$

40. $35 - 5w + 25k = 35 + (-5w) + 25k$
$$= 5(7) + 5(-w) + 5(5k)$$
$$= 5[7 + (-w) + 5k]$$
$$= 5(7 - w + 5k)$$

Lesson 3.6

1. $\dfrac{t}{2} + \dfrac{s}{3}$

2. $\dfrac{15}{23}b - 20$

3. $\dfrac{5r \cdot 7}{15} = \dfrac{35r}{15}$
$$= \dfrac{7r}{3}$$

4. $1.2\left(w + \dfrac{u}{12}\right) = 1.2 \cdot w + 1.2 \cdot \dfrac{u}{12}$
$$= 1.2w + \dfrac{u}{10}$$

5. $\dfrac{9}{14}(6x) - 10 = \dfrac{27}{7}x - 10$

6. $\dfrac{20}{100} \cdot \dfrac{1}{2}w = \dfrac{1}{10}w$

7. $\dfrac{7}{10}(5p \cdot 3) = \dfrac{21p}{2}$

8. $x + \dfrac{3}{4}x + 0.9z = \left(\dfrac{4}{4}x + \dfrac{3}{4}x\right) + 0.9z$

$$= \dfrac{7}{4}x + 0.9z$$

9. $4\left(\dfrac{3}{8}y - \dfrac{1}{2}x\right) = 4\left(\dfrac{3}{8}y\right) + 4\left(-\dfrac{1}{2}x\right)$

$$= \dfrac{3}{2}y + (-2x)$$

$$= \dfrac{3}{2}y - 2x$$

10. $\dfrac{60}{100}\left(\dfrac{4}{6}w - \dfrac{5}{18}v\right) = \dfrac{60}{100}\left(\dfrac{4}{6}w\right) + \dfrac{60}{100}\left(-\dfrac{5}{18}v\right)$

$$= \dfrac{2}{5}w + \left(-\dfrac{1}{6}v\right)$$

$$= \dfrac{2}{5}w - \dfrac{1}{6}v$$

11. Width: $\dfrac{3}{4}(8u - 12) = \dfrac{3}{4}(8u) + \dfrac{3}{4}(-12)$

$$= 6u + (-9)$$
$$= (6u - 9) \text{ in.}$$

The width of the picture frame is $(6u - 9)$ inches.

12.
$$1 \text{ tablespoon} = \dfrac{1}{6} \text{ fl oz}$$

$(10t - 4)$ tablespoons $= \dfrac{1}{6}(10t - 4)$ fl oz

$$= \dfrac{1}{6} \cdot 10t - \dfrac{1}{6} \cdot 4$$

$$= \left(\dfrac{5}{3}t - \dfrac{2}{3}\right) \text{ fl oz}$$

$\left(\dfrac{5}{3}t - \dfrac{2}{3}\right)$ fluid ounces are in $(10t - 4)$

tablespoons.

13. Each person received $\left(\dfrac{11 + w}{7}\right)$ notebooks.

14. The total cost of p pears and p apples is $0.4p + 0.25q$.

15. Number of pencils: $\dfrac{5}{7}q$

There are $\dfrac{5}{7}q$ pencils.

16. Number of diners after 5 adults joined: $y + 5$

Number of children: $\dfrac{5}{8}(y + 5)$

The number of children is $\dfrac{5}{8}(y + 5)$.

17. Cost of camera and lens before tax:
$w + 120$ dollars
Cost of camera and lens including tax:
$1.08(w + 120) = 1.08 \cdot w + 1.08 \cdot 120$
$\qquad\qquad\qquad = (1.08w + 129.6)$ dollars
Freddy paid $(1.08w + 129.6)$ dollars for the camera and lens.

18. Number of cards John has: $\left(5u - \dfrac{8}{13}\right)$

Total number of cards that Emily and
John have: $5u - \dfrac{8}{13} + 5u = (5u + 5u) - \dfrac{8}{13}$

$$= 10u - \dfrac{8}{13}$$

Average number of cards:

$\dfrac{1}{2}\left(10u - \dfrac{8}{13}\right) = \dfrac{1}{2}(10u) + \dfrac{1}{2}\left(-\dfrac{8}{13}\right)$

$$= 5u + \left(-\dfrac{4}{13}\right)$$

$$= 5u - \dfrac{4}{13}$$

Emily and John have an average of
$\left(5u - \dfrac{4}{13}\right)$ game cards.

19. a) Total distance traveled:

$$140 \cdot 2\dfrac{1}{14}x + 3(2x - 3)$$

$$= 140 \cdot \dfrac{29}{14}x + 3(2x) + 3(-3)$$

$$= 290x + 6x + (-9)$$
$$= 290x + 6x - 9$$
$$= (296x - 9) \text{ mi}$$
The total distance traveled by the train is $(296x - 9)$ miles.

b) When $x = 3$, total distance traveled:
$296x - 9 = 296 \cdot 3 - 9 = 879$ mi
The total distance traveled by the train is 879 miles.

Lesson 3.7

1. Difference in length:
$(12.5x + 17) - (5x + 0.4w)$
$= 12.5x + 17 + (-1)(5x) + (-1)(0.4w)$
$= 12.5x + (-1)(5x) + 17 + (-1)(0.4w)$
$= 12.5x - 5x + 17 - 0.4w$
$= (7.5x + 17 - 0.4w)$ cm
The difference in the length of the two ropes is $(7.5x + 17 - 0.4w)$ centimeters.

2. Circumference $= 2\pi r$

$$= 2\left(\frac{22}{7}\right)(7n-21)$$

$$= \left(\frac{44}{7}\right)(7n-21)$$

$$= \left(\frac{44}{7}\right)(7n) + \left(\frac{44}{7}\right)(-21)$$

$$= 44n + (-132)$$

$$= (44n - 132)\,\text{in.}$$

The circumference of the circle is
$(44n - 132)$ inches.

3. Total sales: $4(7.6k + 2.2)$

$$= 4(7.6k) + 4(2.2)$$

$$= (30.4k + 8.8) \text{ dollars}$$

The total sales during the promotion was
$(30.4k + 8.8)$ dollars.

4. Number of yellow ribbons: $\frac{6}{17}(2m+5)$

$$= \frac{6}{17}(2m) + \frac{6}{17}(5)$$

$$= \frac{12}{17}m + 1\frac{13}{17}$$

There are $\frac{12}{17}m + 1\frac{13}{17}$ yellow ribbons.

5. Number of children who went to South
America: $c - 0.36c - 24$

$$= 0.64c - 24$$

$(0.64c - 24)$ children went to South America.

6. Parking fee: $4(1) + 3.2(y - 1)$

$$= 4 + 3.2y + 3.2(-1)$$

$$= 4 + 3.2(-1) + 3.2y$$

$$= 4 - 3.2 + 3.2y$$

$$= (0.8 + 3.2y) \text{ dollars}$$

Her parking fee was $(0.8 + 3.2y)$ dollars.

7. Additional amount of liquid required:

$= (6.9x - 3y + 3) - (4.5x + 2y - 6)$

$= 6.9x - 3y + 3 + (-1)(4.5x) + (-1)(2y) +$
$\quad (-1)(-6)$

$= 6.9x + (-1)(4.5x) - 3y + (-1)(2y) + 3 +$
$\quad (-1)(-6)$

$= 6.9x - 4.5x - 3y - 2y + 3 + 6$

$= (2.4x - 5y + 9) \text{ mL}$

$(2.4x - 5y + 9)$ milliliters of liquid must be
added.

8. Number of girls: $50 - b$

Number of girls younger than 12 years old:
$0.3(50 - b) = 0.3(50) + 0.3(-b)$
$\qquad\qquad\quad = 15 - 0.3b$

Number of boys younger than 12 years old:
$(1 - 0.4)b = 0.6b$

Number of children younger than 12 years old:
$(15 - 0.3b) + 0.6b = 15 - 0.3b + 0.6b$
$\qquad\qquad\qquad\quad = 15 + 0.3b$

$(15 + 0.3b)$ children are younger than
12 years old.

9. Number of koi initially: $\frac{5}{3}b$

Number of fish initially: $\frac{5}{3}b + k$

There were $\left(\frac{5}{3}b + k\right)$ koi and goldfish initially.

10. a) Mass of Bottle B: $\frac{5}{18}(2x - 9)$ kg

b) When $x = 15$, mass of Bottle B:

$$\frac{5}{18}(2x - 9) = \frac{5}{18}(2 \cdot 15 - 9)$$

$$= \frac{5}{18}(30 - 9)$$

$$= \frac{5}{18}(21)$$

$$= \frac{35}{6} \text{ kg}$$

The mass of Bottle B when $x = 15$
is $\frac{35}{6}$ kilograms.

Brain@Work

1. Second number: $\frac{5}{16}\left(\frac{2}{3}x - 12\right)$

$$= \frac{5}{16}\left(\frac{2}{3}x\right) + \frac{5}{16}(-12)$$

$$= \frac{5}{24}x + \left(-\frac{15}{4}\right)$$

$$= \frac{5}{24}x - \frac{15}{4}$$

First number: $\frac{8}{5}\left(\frac{5}{24}x\right) + \frac{8}{5}\left(-\frac{15}{4}\right) - 3$

$$= \frac{8}{5}\left(\frac{5}{24}x\right) + \frac{8}{5}\left(-\frac{15}{4}\right) - 3$$

$$= \frac{1}{3}x - 6 - 3$$

$$= \frac{1}{3}x - 9$$

2. a) $\frac{3}{7}$ of Jar A $\longrightarrow$ $(0.3p + 8)$ pt

$\qquad$ Jar A $\longrightarrow$ $\frac{7}{3}(0.3p + 8)$ pt

The capacity of Jar A is $\frac{7}{3}(0.3p + 8)$ pints.

b) $\frac{1}{2}$ of Jar C $\longrightarrow$ $(0.3p + 8) + 5$

$\qquad\qquad\qquad = (0.3p + 13)$ pt

$\qquad$ Jar C $\longrightarrow$ $2(0.3p + 13)$

$\qquad\qquad\qquad = 2(0.3p) + 2(13)$

$\qquad\qquad\qquad = (0.6p + 26)$ pt

The capacity of Jar C is $(0.6p + 26)$ pints.

Chapter 4

Lesson 4.1

1. $4x + 1 = 9$ and $2x + 1 = 5$

$\qquad 4x + 1 = 9$

$4x + 1 - 1 = 9 - 1$

$\qquad\quad 4x = 8$

$\quad 4x \div 4 = 8 \div 4$

$\qquad\qquad x = 2$

Then check to see if 2 is the solution of the equation $2x + 1 = 5$.

If $x = 2$, $2x + 1 = 2 \cdot 2 + 1$

$\qquad\qquad\qquad = 5$

Because the equations have same solution, they are equivalent equations.

2. $y + 5 = 7$ and $5y = 10$

$\qquad 5y = 10$

$5y \div 5 = 10 \div 5$

$\qquad y = 2$

Then check to see if 2 is the solution of the equation $y + 5 = 7$.

If $y = 2$, $y + 5 = 2 + 5$

$\qquad\qquad\qquad = 7$

Because the equations have same solution, they are equivalent equations.

3. $5z - 3 = 4$ and $z = -1$

If $z = -1$, $5z - 3 = 5 \cdot (-1) - 3$

$\qquad\qquad\qquad\quad = -8 \ (\neq 4)$

Because the equations have different solutions, they are not equivalent equations.

4. $3p - 4 = 8$ and $2p = 4$

$\qquad 2p = 4$

$2p \div 2 = 4 \div 2$

$\qquad p = 2$

Then check to see if 2 is the solution of the equation $3p - 4 = 8$.

If $p = 2$, $3p - 4 = 3 \cdot 2 - 4$

$\qquad\qquad\qquad = 2 \ (\neq 8)$

Because the equations have different solutions, they are not equivalent equations.

5. $7m + 6 - 5 = 15$ and $2m + 5 = 9$

$\qquad\quad 2m + 5 = 9$

$2m + 5 - 5 = 9 - 5$

$\qquad\qquad 2m = 4$

$\qquad 2m \div 2 = 4 \div 2$

$\qquad\qquad\quad m = 2$

Then check to see if 2 is the solution of the equation $7m + 6 - 5 = 15$.

If $m = 2$, $7m + 6 - 5 = 7 \cdot 2 + 6 - 5$

$\qquad\qquad\qquad\qquad = 15$

Because the equations have same solution, they are equivalent equations.

6. $7x + 3 = -4$ and $5x = -5$

$\qquad\quad 5x = -5$

$5x \div 5 = (-5) \div 5$

$\qquad\quad x = -1$

Then check to see if -1 is the solution of the equation $7x + 3 = -4$.

If $x = -1$, $7x + 3 = 7 \cdot (-1) + 3$

$\qquad\qquad\qquad\quad = -4$

Because the equations have same solution, they are equivalent equations.

7. $3x - 5 + 3x = 7$ and $3x + 1 = 7$

$\qquad\quad 3x + 1 = 7$

$3x + 1 - 1 = 7 - 1$

$\qquad\qquad 3x = 6$

$\qquad 3x \div 3 = 6 \div 3$

$\qquad\qquad\quad x = 2$

Then check to see if 2 is the solution of the equation $3x - 5 + 3x = 7$.

If $x = 2$, $3x - 5 + 3x = 3x + 3x - 5$

$\qquad\qquad\qquad\qquad = 6x - 5$

$\qquad\qquad\qquad\qquad = 6 \cdot 2 - 5$

$\qquad\qquad\qquad\qquad = 7$

Because the equations have same solution, they are equivalent equations.

8. $2x - 3 = 0$ and $x + 3 = 0$

$\qquad\quad x + 3 = 0$

$x + 3 - 3 = 0 - 3$

$\qquad\qquad x = -3$

Then check to see if -3 is the solution of the equation $2x - 3 = 0$.

If $x = -3$, $2x - 3 = 2 \cdot (-3) - 3$

$\qquad\qquad\qquad\quad = -9 \ (\neq 0)$

Because the equations have different solutions, they are not equivalent equations.

9. $\frac{2}{5}x - 3 = 1$ and $\frac{3}{4}x = \frac{15}{2}$

$\qquad\qquad \frac{3}{4}x = \frac{15}{2}$

$\qquad \frac{3}{4}x \div \frac{3}{4} = \frac{15}{2} \div \frac{3}{4}$

$\qquad\qquad\quad x = \frac{15}{2} \cdot \frac{4}{3}$

$\qquad\qquad\qquad = 10$

Then check to see if 10 is the solution of the equation $\frac{2}{5}x - 3 = 1$.

If $x = 10$, $\frac{2}{5}x - 3 = \frac{2}{5} \cdot 10 - 3$

$$= 4 - 3$$
$$= 1$$

Because the equations have same solution, they are equivalent equations.

10. $-3x + 4 = 1$ and $x = -1$

If $x = -1$, $-3x + 4 = -3 \cdot (-1) + 4$
$$= 7 \; (\neq 1)$$

Because the equations have different solutions, they are not equivalent equations.

11. $8x = 16$

$8x \div 8 = 16 \div 8$

$x = 2$

So, $8x = 16$ and **b)** are equivalent equations.

12. $x + 3 = 6$

$x + 3 - 3 = 6 - 3$

$x = 3$

$x \cdot 2 = 3 \cdot 2$

$2x = 6$

So, $x + 3 = 6$ and **c)** are equivalent equations.

13. $2x + 13 = 9$

$2x + 13 - 13 = 9 - 13$

$2x = -4$

$2x \div 2 = -4 \div 2$

$x = -2$

$1 + x = 1 + (-2)$

$1 + x = -1$

So, $2x + 13 = 9$ and **e)** are equivalent equations.

14. $4 - 5x = -1$

$4 - 5x - 4 = -1 - 4$

$-5x = -5$

$-5x \div (-5) = -5 \div (-5)$

$x = 1$

So, $4 - 5x = -1$ and **a)** are equivalent equations.

15. $\frac{1}{3}x - 2 = 0$

$\frac{1}{3}x - 2 + 2 = 0 + 2$

$\frac{1}{3}x = 2$

$\frac{1}{3}x \cdot 9 = 2 \cdot 9$

$3x = 18$

$3x - 4 = 18 - 4$

$3x - 4 = 14$

So, $\frac{1}{3}x - 2 = 0$ and **d)** are equivalent equations.

Lesson 4.2

1. $\quad 5x + 3 = 7$

$5x + 3 - 3 = 7 - 3$

$5x = 4$

$5x \div 5 = 4 \div 5$

$x = \frac{4}{5}$

2. $\quad 4y - 7 = 5$

$4y - 7 + 7 = 5 + 7$

$4y = 12$

$4y \div 4 = 12 \div 4$

$y = 3$

3. $\quad 9p + 5 = -13$

$9p + 5 - 5 = -13 - 5$

$9p = -18$

$9p \div 9 = -18 \div 9$

$p = -2$

4. $\quad 23 = 6x - 1$

$23 + 1 = 6x - 1 + 1$

$24 = 6x$

$24 \div 6 = 6x \div 6$

$4 = x$

5. $\quad \frac{2}{3}x - 5 = 1$

$\frac{2}{3}x - 5 + 5 = 1 + 5$

$\frac{2}{3}x = 6$

$\frac{2}{3}x \div \frac{2}{3} = 6 \div \frac{2}{3}$

$x = 6 \cdot \frac{3}{2}$

$x = 9$

6. $\quad \frac{7}{5}y = 3 - \frac{1}{5}$

$\frac{7}{5}y = \frac{15}{5} - \frac{1}{5}$

$\frac{7}{5}y = \frac{14}{5}$

$7y = 14$

$y = 14 \div 7$

$y = 2$

7. $\quad \frac{5}{8}p = \frac{9}{4} - \frac{3}{8}$

$\frac{5}{8}p = \frac{18}{8} - \frac{3}{8}$

$\frac{5}{8}p = \frac{15}{8}$

$5p = 15$

$5p \div 5 = 15 \div 5$

$p = 3$

8.
$$\frac{5}{6} = \frac{3}{4}x - \frac{2}{3}$$
$$\frac{5}{6} + \frac{2}{3} = \frac{3}{4}x - \frac{2}{3} + \frac{2}{3}$$
$$\frac{5}{6} + \frac{4}{6} = \frac{3}{4}x$$
$$\frac{9}{6} = \frac{3}{4}x$$
$$\frac{9}{6} \div \frac{3}{4} = \frac{3}{4}x \div \frac{3}{4}$$
$$\frac{9}{6} \cdot \frac{4}{3} = x$$
$$2 = x$$

9.
$$5.7 + 0.3y = 6.9$$
$$5.7 + 0.3y - 5.7 = 6.9 - 5.7$$
$$0.3y = 1.2$$
$$0.3y \div 0.3 = 1.2 \div 0.3$$
$$y = 4$$

10.
$$4.2 + 2.5a = 9.2$$
$$4.2 + 2.5a - 4.2 = 9.2 - 4.2$$
$$2.5a = 5$$
$$2.5a \div 2.5 = 5 \div 2.5$$
$$a = 2$$

11.
$$3.2y - 7 = 9$$
$$3.2y - 7 + 7 = 9 + 7$$
$$3.2y = 16$$
$$3.2y \div 3.2 = 16 \div 3.2$$
$$y = 5$$

12.
$$5.5p - 6.8 = 15.2$$
$$5.5p - 6.8 + 6.8 = 15.2 + 6.8$$
$$5.5p = 22$$
$$5.5p \div 5.5 = 22 \div 5.5$$
$$p = 4$$

13.
$$3.8x + 5.2x - 6.7 = 11.3$$
$$9x - 6.7 = 11.3$$
$$9x - 6.7 + 6.7 = 11.3 + 6.7$$
$$9x = 18$$
$$9x \div 9 = 18 \div 9$$
$$x = 2$$

14.
$$7.8y - 4.9 - 5.4y = 2.3$$
$$7.8y - 5.4y - 4.9 = 2.3$$
$$2.4y - 4.9 = 2.3$$
$$2.4y - 4.9 + 4.9 = 2.3 + 4.9$$
$$2.4y = 7.2$$
$$2.4y \div 2.4 = 7.2 \div 2.4$$
$$y = 3$$

15.
$$5a + 3 = 2a + 9$$
$$5a + 3 - 2a = 2a + 9 - 2a$$
$$3a + 3 = 9$$
$$3a + 3 - 3 = 9 - 3$$
$$3a = 6$$
$$3a \div 3 = 6 \div 3$$
$$a = 2$$

16.
$$21b + 9 = 15b + 3$$
$$21b + 9 - 15b = 15b + 3 - 15b$$
$$6b + 9 = 3$$
$$6b + 9 - 9 = 3 - 9$$
$$6b = -6$$
$$6b \div 6 = -6 \div 6$$
$$b = -1$$

17.
$$5x - 11 = 12x + 10$$
$$5x - 11 - 5x = 12x + 10 - 5x$$
$$-11 = 7x + 10$$
$$-11 - 10 = 7x + 10 - 10$$
$$-21 = 7x$$
$$-21 \div 7 = 7x \div 7$$
$$-3 = x$$

18.
$$9y - 5 = 15y - 17$$
$$9y - 5 - 9y = 15y - 17 - 9y$$
$$-5 = 6y - 17$$
$$-5 + 17 = 6y - 17 + 17$$
$$12 = 6y$$
$$12 \div 6 = 6y \div 6$$
$$2 = y$$

19.
$$\frac{4}{5}p - 4 = \frac{2}{3}p$$
$$\frac{4}{5}p - 4 - \frac{2}{3}p = \frac{2}{3}p - \frac{2}{3}p$$
$$\frac{12}{15}p - \frac{10}{15}p - 4 = 0$$
$$\frac{2}{15}p - 4 = 0$$
$$\frac{2}{15}p - 4 + 4 = 0 + 4$$
$$\frac{2}{15}p = 4$$
$$\frac{2}{15}p \div \frac{2}{15} = 4 \div \frac{2}{15}$$
$$p = 4 \cdot \frac{15}{2}$$
$$p = 30$$

20.
$$11 + m = \frac{1}{4}m - 2m$$
$$11 + m = \frac{1}{4}m - \frac{8}{4}m$$
$$11 + m = -\frac{7}{4}m$$
$$11 + m - m = -\frac{7}{4}m - m$$
$$11 = -\frac{7}{4}m - \frac{4}{4}m$$
$$11 = -\frac{11}{4}m$$
$$11 \div \left(-\frac{11}{4}\right) = -\frac{11}{4}m \div \left(-\frac{11}{4}\right)$$
$$11 \cdot -\frac{4}{11} = m$$
$$-4 = m$$

21.

$$\frac{1}{3}a - \frac{1}{4} = \frac{5}{6}a - \frac{3}{2}$$

$$\frac{1}{3}a - \frac{1}{4} - \frac{1}{3}a = \frac{5}{6}a - \frac{3}{2} - \frac{1}{3}a$$

$$-\frac{1}{4} = \frac{5}{6}a - \frac{2}{6}a - \frac{3}{2}$$

$$-\frac{1}{4} = \frac{3}{6}a - \frac{3}{2}$$

$$-\frac{1}{4} + \frac{3}{2} = \frac{1}{2}a - \frac{3}{2} + \frac{3}{2}$$

$$-\frac{1}{4} + \frac{6}{4} = \frac{1}{2}a$$

$$\frac{5}{4} = \frac{1}{2}a$$

$$\frac{5}{4} \div \frac{1}{2} = \frac{1}{2}a \div \frac{1}{2}$$

$$\frac{5}{4} \cdot 2 = a$$

$$\frac{5}{2} = a$$

22.

$$\frac{3}{5}m + \frac{1}{4} = m - \frac{1}{4}$$

$$\frac{3}{5}m + \frac{1}{4} - \frac{3}{5}m = m - \frac{1}{4} - \frac{3}{5}m$$

$$\frac{1}{4} = \frac{2}{5}m - \frac{1}{4}$$

$$\frac{1}{4} + \frac{1}{4} = \frac{2}{5}m - \frac{1}{4} + \frac{1}{4}$$

$$\frac{2}{4} = \frac{2}{5}m$$

$$\frac{1}{2} \div \frac{2}{5} = \frac{2}{5}m \div \frac{2}{5}$$

$$\frac{1}{2} \cdot \frac{5}{2} = m$$

$$\frac{5}{4} = m$$

23.

$$2a - 9.3 = 0.8a + 5.1$$
$$2a - 9.3 - 0.8a = 0.8a + 5.1 - 0.8a$$
$$1.2a - 9.3 = 5.1$$
$$1.2a - 9.3 + 9.3 = 5.1 + 9.3$$
$$1.2a = 14.4$$
$$1.2a \div 1.2 = 14.4 \div 1.2$$
$$a = 12$$

24.

$$13.7b - 3 = 3 - 4.3b$$
$$13.7b - 3 + 4.3b = 3 - 4.3b + 4.3b$$
$$18b - 3 = 3$$
$$18b - 3 + 3 = 3 + 3$$
$$18b = 6$$
$$18b \div 18 = 6 \div 18$$
$$b = \frac{1}{3}$$

25.

$$4(3x - 2) = 16$$
$$\frac{1}{4} \cdot 4(3x - 2) = \frac{1}{4} \cdot 16$$
$$3x - 2 = 4$$
$$3x - 2 + 2 = 4 + 2$$
$$3x = 6$$
$$3x \div 3 = 6 \div 3$$
$$x = 2$$

26.

$$24y = 8(1 - 2y)$$
$$\frac{1}{8} \cdot 24y = \frac{1}{8} \cdot 8(1 - 2y)$$
$$3y = 1 - 2y$$
$$3y + 2y = 1 - 2y + 2y$$
$$5y = 1$$
$$5y \div 5 = 1 \div 5$$
$$y = \frac{1}{5}$$

27.

$$3(4x - 1) - 7x = 17$$
$$3 \cdot 4x - 3 \cdot 1 - 7x = 17$$
$$12x - 3 - 7x = 17$$
$$5x - 3 = 17$$
$$5x - 3 + 3 = 17 + 3$$
$$5x = 20$$
$$5x \div 5 = 20 \div 5$$
$$x = 4$$

28.

$$5(2 - 3y) - 9y = 4(3 - 2y)$$
$$5 \cdot 2 - 5 \cdot 3y - 9y = 4 \cdot 3 - 4 \cdot 2y$$
$$10 - 15y - 9y = 12 - 8y$$
$$10 - 24y = 12 - 8y$$
$$10 - 24y + 24y = 12 - 8y + 24y$$
$$10 = 12 + 16y$$
$$10 - 12 = 12 + 16y - 12$$
$$-2 = 16y$$
$$-2 \div 16 = 16y \div 16$$
$$-\frac{1}{8} = y$$

29.

$$\frac{3}{4}(5a - 3) = \frac{3}{8}$$

$$8 \cdot \frac{3}{4}(5a - 3) = 8 \cdot \frac{3}{8}$$

$$6(5a - 3) = 3$$
$$6 \cdot 5a - 6 \cdot 3 = 3$$
$$30a - 18 = 3$$
$$30a - 18 + 18 = 3 + 18$$
$$30a = 21$$
$$30a \div 30 = 21 \div 30$$
$$a = \frac{7}{10}$$

30.

$$\frac{4}{5}(m-1) - \frac{1}{5}m = 1$$

$$5 \cdot \left[\frac{4}{5}(m-1) - \frac{1}{5}m\right] = 5 \cdot 1$$

$$5 \cdot \frac{4}{5}(m-1) - 5 \cdot \frac{1}{5}m = 5$$

$$4(m-1) - m = 5$$

$$4 \cdot m - 4 \cdot 1 - m = 5$$

$$4m - 4 - m = 5$$

$$3m - 4 = 5$$

$$3m - 4 + 4 = 5 + 4$$

$$3m = 9$$

$$3m \div 3 = 9 \div 3$$

$$m = 3$$

31.

$$\frac{2}{5}x - \frac{1}{4}(x - 8) = \frac{13}{2}$$

$$20 \cdot \left[\frac{2}{5}x - \frac{1}{4}(x - 8)\right] = 20 \cdot \frac{13}{2}$$

$$20 \cdot \frac{2}{5}x - 20 \cdot \frac{1}{4}(x - 8) = 130$$

$$8x - 5(x - 8) = 130$$

$$8x - 5 \cdot x - 5 \cdot (-8) = 130$$

$$8x - 5x + 40 = 130$$

$$3x + 40 = 130$$

$$3x + 40 - 40 = 130 - 40$$

$$3x = 90$$

$$3x \div 3 = 90 \div 3$$

$$x = 30$$

32.

$$6(3.2y - 1) = 3.6$$

$$6 \cdot 3.2y - 6 \cdot 1 = 3.6$$

$$19.2y - 6 = 3.6$$

$$19.2y - 6 + 6 = 3.6 + 6$$

$$19.2y = 9.6$$

$$19.2y \div 19.2 = 9.6 \div 19.2$$

$$y = 0.5$$

33.

$$1.8(5a + 3) + 5.6 = 29$$

$$1.8 \cdot 5a + 1.8 \cdot 3 + 5.6 = 29$$

$$9a + 5.4 + 5.6 = 29$$

$$9a + 11 = 29$$

$$9a + 11 - 11 = 29 - 11$$

$$9a = 18$$

$$9a \div 9 = 18 \div 9$$

$$a = 2$$

34.

$$0.4(2x - 3) = 0.2x$$

$$0.4 \cdot 2x - 0.4 \cdot 3 = 0.2x$$

$$0.8x - 1.2 = 0.2x$$

$$0.8x - 1.2 - 0.2x = 0.2x - 0.2x$$

$$0.6x - 1.2 = 0$$

$$0.6x - 1.2 + 1.2 = 0 + 1.2$$

$$0.6x = 1.2$$

$$0.6x \div 0.6 = 1.2 \div 0.6$$

$$x = 2$$

35.

$$0.5(2m - 3) - 0.8m = 2.7$$

$$0.5 \cdot 2m - 0.5 \cdot 3 - 0.8m = 2.7$$

$$m - 1.5 - 0.8m = 2.7$$

$$0.2m - 1.5 = 2.7$$

$$0.2m - 1.5 + 1.5 = 2.7 + 1.5$$

$$0.2m = 4.2$$

$$0.2m \div 0.2 = 4.2 \div 0.2$$

$$m = 21$$

36.

$$0.8(4p + 5) = 4(0.5p - 2)$$

$$0.8 \cdot 4p + 0.8 \cdot 5 = 4 \cdot 0.5p - 4 \cdot 2$$

$$3.2p + 4 = 2p - 8$$

$$3.2p + 4 - 2p = 2p - 8 - 2p$$

$$1.2p + 4 = -8$$

$$1.2p + 4 - 4 = -8 - 4$$

$$1.2p = -12$$

$$1.2p \div 1.2 = -12 \div 1.2$$

$$p = -10$$

Lesson 4.3

1. Let x represent the amount of money, in dollars, Amy had initially.
Because Amy had $139 after Sam gave her $27,

$$x + 27 = 139$$

$$x + 27 - 27 = 139 - 27$$

$$x = 112$$

Amy had $112 initially.

2. Let the two facing page numbers be x and $(x + 1)$.
Because the sum of the two facing page numbers is 145,

$$x + (x + 1) = 145$$

$$x + x + 1 = 145$$

$$2x + 1 = 145$$

$$2x + 1 - 1 = 145 - 1$$

$$2x = 144$$

$$2x \div 2 = 144 \div 2$$

$$x = 72$$

If $x = 72$, $x + 1 = 72 + 1$
$= 73$

The two page numbers are 72 and 73.

3. Let Jackson's age now be x years old.

Because 7 years ago, Jackson's age was $\frac{2}{5}$ of the age he will be in 20 years from now,

$$x - 7 = \frac{2}{5}(x + 20)$$
$$5(x - 7) = 5\left[\frac{2}{5}(x + 20)\right]$$
$$5(x - 7) = 2(x + 20)$$
$$5 \cdot x - 5 \cdot 7 = 2 \cdot x + 2 \cdot 20$$
$$5x - 35 = 2x + 40$$
$$5x - 35 - 2x = 2x + 40 - 2x$$
$$3x - 35 = 40$$
$$3x - 35 + 35 = 40 + 35$$
$$3x = 75$$
$$3x \div 3 = 75 \div 3$$
$$x = 25$$

Jackson is 25 years old now.

4. Let the length of each of the other two sides of the isosceles triangle be l inches.
Because the base is 9.5 inches and the perimeter of the isosceles triangle is 32.7 inches,
$$l + l + 9.5 = 32.7$$
$$2l + 9.5 = 32.7$$
$$2l + 9.5 - 9.5 = 32.7 - 9.5$$
$$2l = 23.2$$
$$2l \div 2 = 23.2 \div 2$$
$$l = 11.6 \text{ in.}$$
The length of each of the other two sides is 11.6 inches.

5. Let r represent the number of raisin muffins.

The number of chocolate muffins is $\frac{1}{2}r$.

The number of strawberry muffins is $\frac{3}{2}r$.

If she only had enough ingredients to bake 480 muffins,
$$\frac{1}{2}r + r + \frac{3}{2}r = 480$$
$$3r = 480$$
$$3r \div 3 = 480 \div 3$$
$$r = 160$$
She baked 160 raisin muffins.

6. Let the number of miles Mr. Sidney drove be d miles.
Because he paid a total of $52.54,
$$19.99 + 0.21d = 52.54$$
$$19.99 + 0.21d - 19.99 = 52.54 - 19.99$$
$$0.21d = 32.55$$
$$0.21d \div 0.21 = 32.55 \div 0.21$$
$$d = 155$$
Mr. Sidney drove the car for 155 miles.

7. Let the number of product labels collected in the third month be n.
Then the number of product labels collected in the first two months is $3n$ each.
Because the total number of product labels collected in three months is 2,100,
$$3n + 3n + n = 2,100$$
$$7n = 2,100$$
$$7n \div 7 = 2,100 \div 7$$
$$n = 300$$
300 product labels were collected in the third month.

8. Because the perimeter of the triangle is 33 inches,
$$2x + 2(x + 3) + 3(x + 2) = 33$$
$$2x + 2 \cdot x + 2 \cdot 3 + 3 \cdot x + 3 \cdot 2 = 33$$
$$2x + 2x + 6 + 3x + 6 = 33$$
$$7x + 12 = 33$$
$$7x + 12 - 12 = 33 - 12$$
$$7x = 21$$
$$7x \div 7 = 21 \div 7$$
$$x = 3$$
If $x = 3$, $2x = 2 \cdot 3$
$$= 6$$
The length of AB is 6 inches.
If $x = 3$, $2(x + 3) = 2(3 + 3)$
$$= 2 \cdot 6$$
$$= 12$$
The length of BC is 12 inches.
If $x = 3$, $3(x + 2) = 3(3 + 2)$
$$= 3 \cdot 5$$
$$= 15$$
The length of AC is 15 inches.

9. Let the airfare be m dollars.
Then the expenses on food, gifts, and accommodation was $(3m - 80)$ dollars.
Because the total expenses for the trip was $2,660,
$$m + (3m - 80) = 2,660$$
$$m + 3m - 80 = 2,660$$
$$4m - 80 = 2,660$$
$$4m - 80 + 80 = 2,660 + 80$$
$$4m = 2,740$$
$$4m \div 4 = 2,740 \div 4$$
$$m = 685$$
Her airfare was $685.

10. Distance = Speed · Time

So, Time = Distance ÷ Speed

Because the total time taken for the journey is $7\frac{3}{4}$ hours,

$$\frac{d}{16} + \frac{d}{15} = 7\frac{3}{4}$$

$$\frac{d}{16} + \frac{d}{15} = \frac{31}{4}$$

$$240 \cdot \left[\frac{d}{16} + \frac{d}{15}\right] = 240 \cdot \frac{31}{4}$$

$$240 \cdot \frac{d}{16} + 240 \cdot \frac{d}{15} = 1{,}860$$

$$15d + 16d = 1{,}860$$

$$31d = 1{,}860$$

$$31d \div 31 = 1{,}860 \div 31$$

$$d = 60 \text{ km}$$

Total distance traveled = $d + d$

$\qquad\qquad\qquad = 2d$ km

If $d = 60$, $d = 2 \cdot 60$

$\qquad\qquad = 120$ km

The total distance traveled by him is 120 kilometers.

Lesson 4.4

1.
$$27 + y < 10$$
$$27 + y - 27 < 10 - 27$$
$$y < -17$$

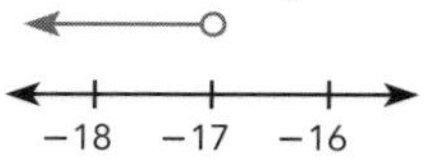

（number line with open circle at −17, arrow left; marks −18, −17, −16）

2.
$$4x + 5 \geq 29$$
$$4x + 5 - 5 \geq 29 - 5$$
$$4x \geq 24$$
$$4x \div 4 \geq 24 \div 4$$
$$x \geq 6$$

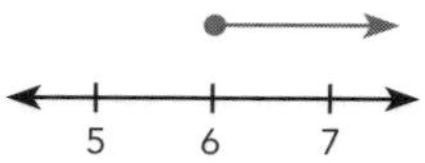

（number line with closed circle at 6, arrow right; marks 5, 6, 7）

3.
$$6y + 1 > 7$$
$$6y + 1 - 1 > 7 - 1$$
$$6y > 6$$
$$6y \div 6 > 6 \div 6$$
$$y > 1$$

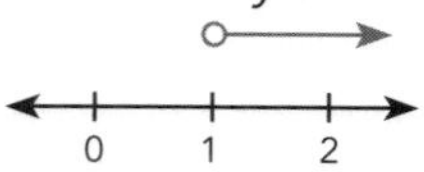

（number line with open circle at 1, arrow right; marks 0, 1, 2）

4.
$$3p + 1 \leq -1$$
$$3p + 1 - 1 \leq -1 - 1$$
$$3p \leq -2$$

$$3p \div 3 \leq -2 \div 3$$

$$p \leq -\frac{2}{3}$$

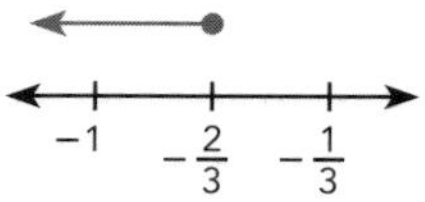

（number line with closed circle at $-\frac{2}{3}$, arrow left; marks −1, $-\frac{2}{3}$, $-\frac{1}{3}$）

5.
$$9 \geq 12 - x$$
$$9 + x \geq 12 - x + x$$
$$9 + x \geq 12$$
$$9 + x - 9 \geq 12 - 9$$
$$x \geq 3$$

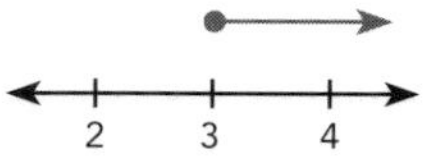

（number line with closed circle at 3, arrow right; marks 2, 3, 4）

6.
$$3 - 5x > 13$$
$$3 - 5x - 3 > 13 - 3$$
$$-5x > 10$$
$$-5x \div (-5) < 10 \div (-5)$$
$$x < -2$$

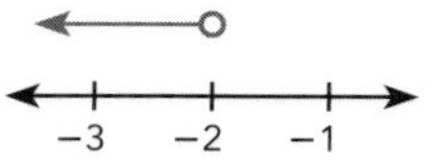

（number line with open circle at −2, arrow left; marks −3, −2, −1）

7.
$$\frac{5}{6}x - \frac{1}{2} < \frac{1}{3}$$
$$\frac{5}{6}x - \frac{1}{2} + \frac{1}{2} < \frac{1}{3} + \frac{1}{2}$$
$$\frac{5}{6}x < \frac{2}{6} + \frac{3}{6}$$
$$\frac{5}{6}x < \frac{5}{6}$$
$$\frac{5}{6}x \cdot \frac{6}{5} < \frac{5}{6} \cdot \frac{6}{5}$$
$$x < 1$$

（number line with open circle at 1, arrow left; marks 0, 1, 2）

8.
$$\frac{7}{8} - \frac{1}{4}x \geq \frac{3}{4}$$
$$\frac{7}{8} - \frac{1}{4}x - \frac{7}{8} \geq \frac{3}{4} - \frac{7}{8}$$
$$-\frac{1}{4}x \geq \frac{6}{8} - \frac{7}{8}$$
$$-\frac{1}{4}x \geq -\frac{1}{8}$$
$$-\frac{1}{4}x \cdot (-4) \leq -\frac{1}{8} \cdot (-4)$$
$$x \leq \frac{1}{2}$$

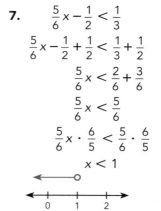

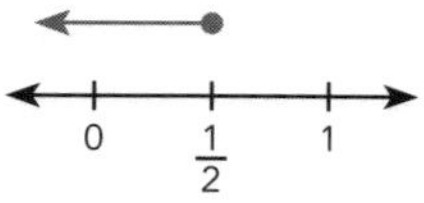

（number line with closed circle at $\frac{1}{2}$, arrow left; marks 0, $\frac{1}{2}$, 1）

9. $\frac{4}{5}y - \frac{1}{5} > 3$

$\frac{4}{5}y - \frac{1}{5} + \frac{1}{5} > 3 + \frac{1}{5}$

$\frac{4}{5}y > 3\frac{1}{5}$

$\frac{4}{5}y > \frac{16}{5}$

$\frac{4}{5}y \cdot \frac{5}{4} > \frac{16}{5} \cdot \frac{5}{4}$

$y > 4$

10. $3x + 3 > 7 + x$

$3x + 3 - 3 > 7 + x - 3$

$3x > 4 + x$

$3x - x > 4 + x - x$

$2x > 4$

$2x \div 2 > 4 \div 2$

$x > 2$

11. $8 - x < 10 - 2x$

$8 - x + 2x < 10 - 2x + 2x$

$8 + x < 10$

$8 + x - 8 < 10 - 8$

$x < 2$

12. $11 + x \le 7 + 5x$

$11 + x - x \le 7 + 5x - x$

$11 \le 7 + 4x$

$11 - 7 \le 7 + 4x - 7$

$4 \le 4x$

$4 \div 4 \le 4x \div 4$

$1 \le x$

13. $0.3x - 7 < 11 + 0.2x$

$0.3x - 7 + 7 < 11 + 0.2x + 7$

$0.3x < 18 + 0.2x$

$0.3x - 0.2x < 18 + 0.2x - 0.2x$

$0.1x < 18$

$0.1x \div 0.1 < 18 \div 0.1$

$x < 180$

14. $2.8x + 7 \ge 4.8x + 9$

$2.8x + 7 - 7 \ge 4.8x + 9 - 7$

$2.8x \ge 4.8x + 2$

$2.8x - 2.8x \ge 4.8x + 2 - 2.8x$

$0 \ge 2x + 2$

$0 - 2 \ge 2x + 2 - 2$

$-2 \ge 2x$

$-2 \div 2 \ge 2x \div 2$

$-1 \ge x$

15. $11.3 - 0.5x > 12 - 0.4x$

$11.3 - 0.5x + 0.4x > 12 - 0.4x + 0.4x$

$11.3 - 0.1x > 12$

$11.3 - 0.1x - 11.3 > 12 - 11.3$

$-0.1x > 0.7$

$-0.1x \div (-0.1) < 0.7 \div (-0.1)$

$x < -7$

16. $\frac{3}{4}x + \frac{3}{4} \ge \frac{1}{2}x + 12.4$

$\frac{3}{4}x + \frac{3}{4} - \frac{3}{4} \ge \frac{1}{2}x + 12.4 - \frac{3}{4}$

$\frac{3}{4}x \ge \frac{1}{2}x + 12\frac{2}{5} - \frac{3}{4}$

$\frac{3}{4}x \ge \frac{1}{2}x + \frac{62}{5} - \frac{3}{4}$

$20 \cdot \left(\frac{3}{4}x\right) \ge 20 \cdot \left(\frac{1}{2}x + \frac{62}{5} - \frac{3}{4}\right)$

$15x \ge 20 \cdot \frac{1}{2}x + 20 \cdot \frac{62}{5} - 20 \cdot \frac{3}{4}$

$15x \ge 10x + 248 - 15$

$15x \ge 10x + 233$

$15x - 10x \ge 10x + 233 - 10x$

$5x \ge 233$

$5x \div 5 \ge 233 \div 5$

$x \ge 46.6$

17. $\frac{4}{7}x + 3 < \frac{5}{7}x + 4$

$\frac{4}{7}x + 3 - \frac{4}{7}x < \frac{5}{7}x + 4 - \frac{4}{7}x$

$3 < \frac{1}{7}x + 4$

$3 - 4 < \frac{1}{7}x + 4 - 4$

$-1 < \frac{1}{7}x$

$-1 \cdot 7 < \frac{1}{7}x \cdot 7$

$-7 < x$

18. $\frac{5}{6}x + \frac{1}{3} < \frac{2}{3}x + 1$

$6 \cdot \left(\frac{5}{6}x + \frac{1}{3}\right) < 6 \cdot \left(\frac{2}{3}x + 1\right)$

$6 \cdot \frac{5}{6}x + 6 \cdot \frac{1}{3} < 6 \cdot \frac{2}{3}x + 6 \cdot 1$

$5x + 2 < 4x + 6$

$5x + 2 - 4x < 4x + 6 - 4x$

$x + 2 < 6$

$x + 2 - 2 < 6 - 2$

$x < 4$

19.
$$3(y + 2) \leq 18$$
$$\frac{1}{3} \cdot 3(y + 2) \leq \frac{1}{3} \cdot 18$$
$$y + 2 \leq 6$$
$$y + 2 - 2 \leq 6 - 2$$
$$y \leq 4$$

20.
$$6(2y - 1) > 3.6$$
$$\frac{1}{6} \cdot 6(2y - 1) > \frac{1}{6} \cdot 3.6$$
$$2y - 1 > 0.6$$
$$2y - 1 + 1 > 0.6 + 1$$
$$2y > 1.6$$
$$2y \div 2 > 1.6 \div 2$$
$$y > 0.8$$

21.
$$2(9 - x) \leq 16 - x$$
$$2 \cdot 9 - 2 \cdot x \leq 16 - x$$
$$18 - 2x \leq 16 - x$$
$$18 - 2x + 2x \leq 16 - x + 2x$$
$$18 \leq 16 + x$$
$$18 - 16 \leq 16 + x - 16$$
$$2 \leq x$$

22.
$$2(2y - 3) - 4 \geq y - 2$$
$$2 \cdot 2y - 2 \cdot 3 - 4 \geq y - 2$$
$$4y - 6 - 4 \geq y - 2$$
$$4y - 10 \geq y - 2$$
$$4y - 10 - y \geq y - 2 - y$$
$$3y - 10 \geq -2$$
$$3y - 10 + 10 \geq -2 + 10$$
$$3y \geq 8$$
$$3y \div 3 \geq 8 \div 3$$
$$y \geq \frac{8}{3}$$

23.
$$\frac{1}{6}(a - 1) > 2(a - 1)$$
$$6 \cdot \frac{1}{6}(a - 1) > 6 \cdot 2(a - 1)$$
$$a - 1 > 12(a - 1)$$
$$a - 1 > 12 \cdot a - 12 \cdot 1$$
$$a - 1 > 12a - 12$$
$$a - 1 - a > 12a - 12 - a$$
$$-1 > 11a - 12$$
$$-1 + 12 > 11a - 12 + 12$$
$$11 > 11a$$
$$11 \div 11 > 11a \div 11$$
$$1 > a$$

24.
$$7(2a - 3) \leq 5 - 2(3a - 1)$$
$$7 \cdot 2a - 7 \cdot 3 \leq 5 - 2 \cdot 3a - 2 \cdot (-1)$$
$$14a - 21 \leq 5 - 6a + 2$$
$$14a - 21 \leq 7 - 6a$$
$$14a - 21 + 6a \leq 7 - 6a + 6a$$
$$20a - 21 \leq 7$$
$$20a - 21 + 21 \leq 7 + 21$$
$$20a \leq 28$$
$$20a \div 20 \leq 28 \div 20$$
$$a \leq 1.4$$

25.
$$2(2y - 3) < 4 + 3(y - 2)$$
$$2 \cdot 2y + 2 \cdot (-3) < 4 + 3 \cdot y + 3 \cdot (-2)$$
$$4y - 6 < 4 + 3y - 6$$
$$4y - 6 < 3y - 2$$
$$4y - 6 - 3y < 3y - 2 - 3y$$
$$y - 6 < -2$$
$$y - 6 + 6 < -2 + 6$$
$$y < 4$$

26.
$$8 + 5(z - 4) < 2(z + 7)$$
$$8 + 5 \cdot z - 5 \cdot 4 < 2 \cdot z + 2 \cdot 7$$
$$8 + 5z - 20 < 2z + 14$$
$$-12 + 5z < 2z + 14$$
$$-12 + 5z - 2z < 2z + 14 - 2z$$
$$-12 + 3z < 14$$
$$-12 + 3z + 12 < 14 + 12$$
$$3z < 26$$
$$3z \cdot \frac{1}{3} < 26 \cdot \frac{1}{3}$$
$$z < \frac{26}{3}$$

Lesson 4.5

1. Let x be the score he gets on the next quiz.
$$\text{Average} \geq 80$$
$$\frac{1}{5} \cdot (70 + 75 + 83 + 80 + x) \geq 80$$
$$\frac{1}{5} \cdot (308 + x) \geq 80$$
$$5 \cdot \frac{1}{5} \cdot (308 + x) \geq 5 \cdot 80$$
$$308 + x \geq 400$$
$$308 + x - 308 \geq 400 - 308$$
$$x \geq 92$$
He must get at least 92 on the next quiz.

2. Let Howard's weekly savings be x dollars.

$$\text{Total savings} \geq 245$$
$$28 + 9x \geq 245$$
$$28 + 9x - 28 \geq 245 - 28$$
$$9x \geq 217$$
$$9x \div 9 \geq 217 \div 9$$
$$x \geq 24\frac{1}{9}$$

He must save at least $25 each week.

3. Let the length of talk time after the first three minutes be t.

$$\text{Total call charges} \leq 3.60$$
$$0.75 + 0.12t \leq 3.60$$
$$0.75 + 0.12t - 0.75 \leq 3.60 - 0.75$$
$$0.12t \leq 2.85$$
$$0.12t \div 0.12 \leq 2.85 \div 0.12$$
$$t \leq 23.75$$

The greatest possible length of talk time after the first three minutes is 23 minutes. Therefore, the greatest possible length of talk time is 26 minutes.

4. Let h be the number of hours.
Because she plans to donate at most $85,

$$50 + 15h \leq 85$$
$$50 + 15h - 50 \leq 85 - 50$$
$$15h \leq 35$$
$$15h \div 15 \leq 35 \div 15$$
$$h \leq 2\frac{1}{3}$$

She can spend at most 2 hours in the balloon ride.

5. Let the number of chairs be m.
The number of stools is $(m - 25)$.

$$\text{Total cost} \leq 2{,}620$$
$$32m + 28(m - 25) \leq 2{,}620$$
$$32m + 28 \cdot m - 28 \cdot 25 \leq 2{,}620$$
$$32m + 28m - 700 \leq 2{,}620$$
$$60m - 700 \leq 2{,}620$$
$$60m - 700 + 700 \leq 2{,}620 + 700$$
$$60m \leq 3{,}320$$
$$60m \div 60 \leq 3{,}320 \div 60$$
$$m \leq 55\frac{1}{3}$$

They can buy at most 55 chairs.

Brain@Work

1. Let an integer be x.

The other integer is $\frac{3}{4}x + 15$.

Because the sum of the integers is greater than 49,

$$x + \left(\frac{3}{4}x + 15\right) > 49$$
$$x + \frac{3}{4}x + 15 > 49$$
$$\frac{4}{4}x + \frac{3}{4}x + 15 > 49$$
$$\frac{7}{4}x + 15 > 49$$
$$\frac{7}{4}x + 15 - 15 > 49 - 15$$
$$\frac{7}{4}x > 34$$
$$\frac{7}{4}x \cdot \frac{4}{7} > 34 \cdot \frac{4}{7}$$
$$x > \frac{136}{7}$$
$$x > 19\frac{3}{7}$$

The smallest integer x can be is 20.

If $x = 20$, $\frac{3}{4}x + 15 = \frac{3}{4} \cdot 20 + 15$
$$= 30$$

The least values for these two integers are 20 and 30.

2. Let the number of hours be d.
For Plan A to be a better option,

$$\text{Rental for Plan A} < \text{Rental for Plan B}$$
$$210 + 10d < 120 + 25d$$
$$210 + 10d - 10d < 120 + 25d - 10d$$
$$210 < 120 + 15d$$
$$210 - 120 < 120 + 15d - 120$$
$$90 < 15d$$
$$90 \div 15 < 15d \div 15$$
$$6 < d$$

Josie would have to rent the photo booth for more than 6 hours for Plan A to be a better option.

3. Let the number of adults be x.
The number of children is $3x$.

$$\text{Box office receipts} \leq 3{,}190$$
$$8.50x + 5.50 \cdot (3x) \leq 3{,}190$$
$$8.50x + 16.50x \leq 3{,}190$$
$$25x \leq 3{,}190$$
$$25x \div 25 \leq 3{,}190 \div 25$$
$$x \leq 127.6$$

The greatest number of adult tickets sold was 127.

Chapter 5

Lesson 5.1

1. For each pair of x and y:

   $\dfrac{y}{x} = \dfrac{4}{1} = 4; \dfrac{y}{x} = \dfrac{8}{2} = 4; \dfrac{y}{x} = \dfrac{12}{3} = 4$

   Yes, y is directly proportional to x.
   The constant of proportionality is 4.
   The direct proportion equation is $y = 4x$.

2. For each pair of x and y:

   $\dfrac{y}{x} = \dfrac{160}{2} = 80; \dfrac{y}{x} = \dfrac{120}{4} = 30; \dfrac{y}{x} = \dfrac{80}{6} = 13\dfrac{1}{3}$

   No, y is not directly proportional to x.

3. For each pair of x and y:

   $\dfrac{y}{x} = \dfrac{10}{3} = 3\dfrac{1}{3}; \dfrac{y}{x} = \dfrac{30}{6} = 5; \dfrac{y}{x} = \dfrac{70}{9} = 7\dfrac{7}{9}$

   No, y is not directly proportional to x.

4. For each pair of x and y:

   $\dfrac{y}{x} = \dfrac{40}{2} = 20; \dfrac{y}{x} = \dfrac{80}{4} = 20; \dfrac{y}{x} = \dfrac{120}{6} = 20$

   Yes, y is directly proportional to x.
   The constant of proportionality is 20.
   The direct proportion equation is $y = 20x$.

5. $\dfrac{1}{4}y = 5x$

   $4 \cdot \dfrac{1}{4}y = 4 \cdot 5x$

   $y = 20x$

   Yes, y is directly proportional to x.
   The constant of proportionality is 20.

6. $3y + 7 = x$

   $3y + 7 - 7 = x - 7$

   $3y = x - 7$

   $\dfrac{1}{3} \cdot 3y = \dfrac{1}{3}(x - 7)$

   $y = \dfrac{1}{3}(x - 7)$

   No, y is not directly proportional to x.

7. Yes, a is directly proportional to b.
   The constant of proportionality is 1.2.

8. $2.5p = q - 1.6$

   $\dfrac{2.5p}{2.5} = \dfrac{(q - 1.6)}{2.5}$

   $p = \dfrac{2}{5}(q - 1.6)$

   No, p is not directly proportional to q.

9. For each pair of n and t:

   $\dfrac{n}{t} = \dfrac{30}{12} = 2.5; \dfrac{n}{t} = \dfrac{60}{24} = 2.5; \dfrac{n}{t} = \dfrac{75}{30} = 2.5$

   Yes, n is directly proportional to t.
   The constant of proportionality is 2.5.
   The direct proportion equation is $n = 2.5t$.

10. For each pair of d and t:

    $\dfrac{d}{t} = \dfrac{50}{1} = 50; \dfrac{d}{t} = \dfrac{110}{2} = 55; \dfrac{d}{t} = \dfrac{200}{3} = 66\dfrac{2}{3}$

    No, d is not directly proportional to t.

11. The constant of proportionality is 8.5.
    The direct proportion equation is $C = 8.5n$.

12. The constant of proportionality is 21.
    The direct proportion equation is $w = 21n$.

13. Constant of proportionality: $\dfrac{a}{b} = \dfrac{14}{42} = \dfrac{1}{3}$;

    Direct proportion equation: $a = \dfrac{1}{3}b$

14. Constant of proportionality: $\dfrac{w}{v} = \dfrac{6}{10} = \dfrac{3}{5}$;

    Direct proportion equation: $w = \dfrac{3}{5}v$

15. Constant of proportionality: $\dfrac{60.80}{4} = 15.2$;

    Answers vary. Sample: $y = 15.2x$;
    $w = 15.2h$

16. Constant of proportionality: $\dfrac{1}{3}$;

    Answers vary. Sample: $y = \dfrac{1}{3}x; v = \dfrac{1}{3}t$

Lesson 5.2

1. Yes; $\dfrac{y}{x} = 1$ 2. No   3. No

4. Yes; $\dfrac{y}{x} = 100$ 5. No   6. No

7. a) $\dfrac{w}{t} = 20$; It represents the amount Joe earns per hour.

   b) From the graph, Joe earns $60 for 3 hours of work.

   c) $\dfrac{90}{20} = 4.5$ h

   Joe works for 4.5 hours if he earns $90.

8. a) $\dfrac{h}{x} = 2$; it represents the daily growth rate of a seedling.

   b) $h = 2x$

   c) On Day 5, the seedling has a height of 10 centimeters.

d) The height of the seedling after 3 days is 6 centimeters; after one week is 14 centimeters.

e) It will take 9 days for the seedling to reach a height of at least 18 centimeters.

9.

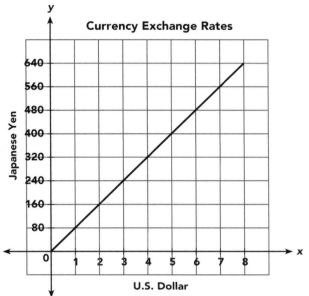

Currency Exchange Rates

(x-axis: U.S. Dollar; y-axis: Japanese Yen)

a) Yes

b) 80 Japanese yen per U.S. dollar

c) $y = 80x$

d) From the graph, Yuki receives 6 U.S. dollars when she exchanges 480 Japanese yen for U.S. dollars.

e) From the graph, Justin receives 720 Japanese yen when he exchanges 9 U.S. dollars for Japanese yen.

Lesson 5.3

1. a) Constant of proportionality: $\dfrac{a}{b} = \dfrac{4}{24} = \dfrac{1}{6}$;

Direct proportion equation: $a = \dfrac{1}{6}b$

b) $a = \dfrac{1}{6} \cdot 63$

$a = 10\dfrac{1}{2}$

c) $7 = \dfrac{1}{6}b$

$7 \cdot 6 = \dfrac{1}{6}b \cdot 6$

$42 = b$

2. a) Constant of proportionality: $\dfrac{w}{v} = \dfrac{32}{80} = \dfrac{2}{5}$;

Direct proportion equation: $w = \dfrac{2}{5}v$

b) $w = \dfrac{2}{5} \cdot 120$

$w = 48$

c) $25 = \dfrac{2}{5}v$

$25 \cdot \dfrac{5}{2} = \dfrac{2}{5}v \cdot \dfrac{5}{2}$

$62\dfrac{1}{2} = v$

3. a) Constant of proportionality: $\dfrac{y}{x} = \dfrac{18}{\left(\dfrac{1}{2}\right)} = 36$;

Direct proportion equation: $y = 36x$

b) $252 = 36x$

$252 \div 36 = 36x \div 36$

$7 = x$

c) $y = 36 \cdot \dfrac{1}{3}$

$y = 12$

4.

p	20	40	80
q	4	8	16

Constant of proportionality: $\dfrac{q}{p} = \dfrac{4}{20} = \dfrac{1}{5}$;

Direct proportion equation: $q = \dfrac{1}{5}p$

When $p = 40$ and $q = \dfrac{1}{5}p$,

$q = \dfrac{1}{5} \cdot 40$

$q = 8$

When $q = 16$ and $q = \dfrac{1}{5}p$,

$16 = \dfrac{1}{5}p$,

$16 \cdot 5 = \dfrac{1}{5}p \cdot 5$

$80 = p$

5.

p	1	3	10
q	9	27	90

Constant of proportionality: $\dfrac{q}{p} = \dfrac{27}{3} = 9$;

Direct proportion equation: $q = 9p$

When $p = 1$ and $q = 9p$,
$q = 9 \cdot 1$
$q = 9$
When $q = 90$ and $q = 9p$,
$90 = 9p$
$90 \div 9 = 9p \div 9$
$10 = p$

6. **a)** $\dfrac{\$96}{12} = \$8$

   The cost of a baseball cap is $8.

   b) $C = 8n$

   c) When $n = 20$ and $C = 8n$,
   $C = 8 \cdot 20$
   $C = 160$

7. **a)** $\dfrac{\$120}{6} = \$20$

   Each person donated $20.

   b) $A = 20n$

   c) When $n = 50$ and $A = 20n$,
   $A = 20 \cdot 50$
   $A = 1{,}000$
   50 people donated $1,000.

8. **a)** $\dfrac{275}{5} = 55$

   b) $w = 55t$

   c) When $w = 935$ and $w = 55t$,
   $935 = 55t$
   $935 \div 55 = 55t \div 55$
   $17 \text{ min} = t$

   She will take 17 minutes to type a 935-word document.

9. **a)** $\dfrac{8}{5}$ or 1.6

   b) $h = \dfrac{8}{5}d$ or $h = 1.6d$

   c) When $d = 12$ and $h = 1.6d$,
   $h = 1.6 \cdot 12$
   $h = 19.2 \text{ ft}$

   The height of the tree is 19.2 feet.

10. Let C be the cost of one dozen cans of grapefruit juice.

$$\frac{C \text{ dollars}}{12 \text{ cans}} = \frac{\$3.36}{4 \text{ cans}}$$

$$\frac{C}{12} = \frac{3.36}{4}$$

$$12 \cdot \frac{C}{12} = 12 \cdot \frac{3.36}{4}$$

$$C = 10.08$$

The cost of one dozen cans of grapefruit juice is $10.08.

11. Let C be the cost of renting the skis for a week.

$$\frac{C \text{ dollars}}{7 \text{ days}} = \frac{\$78}{3 \text{ days}}$$

$$\frac{C}{7} = \frac{78}{3}$$

$$7 \cdot \frac{C}{7} = 7 \cdot \frac{78}{3}$$

$$C = 182$$

The cost of renting the skis for a week is $182.

12. Let x be the distance traveled.

$$\frac{x \text{ mi}}{2\frac{1}{2} \text{ h}} = \frac{14 \text{ mi}}{1 \text{ h}}$$

$$\frac{x}{\left(2\frac{1}{2}\right)} = \frac{14}{1}$$

$$2\frac{1}{2} \cdot \frac{x}{\left(2\frac{1}{2}\right)} = 2\frac{1}{2} \cdot \frac{14}{1}$$

$$x = \frac{5}{2} \cdot 14$$

$$x = 35 \text{ mi}$$

He will ride 35 miles in $2\frac{1}{2}$ hours.

13. Let y be the amount of orange juice that Susannah uses.

$$\frac{5 \text{ oz of lemonade}}{9 \text{ oz of orange juice}} = \frac{40 \text{ oz of lemonade}}{y \text{ oz of orange juice}}$$

$$\frac{5}{9} = \frac{40}{y}$$

$$5 \cdot y = 40 \cdot 9$$

$$5y = 360$$

$$5y \div 5 = 360 \div 5$$

$$y = 72 \text{ oz}$$

She uses 72 ounces of orange juice.

14. Let y be the number of T-shirts.

$$\frac{80 \text{ T-shirts}}{10 \text{ min}} = \frac{y \text{ T-shirts}}{60 \text{ min}}$$

$$\frac{80}{10} = \frac{y}{60}$$

$$10 \cdot y = 80 \cdot 60$$

$$10y = 4{,}800$$

$$10y \div 10 = 4{,}800 \div 10$$

$$y = 480$$

The machine can print 480 T-shirts in an hour.

15. Let y be the amount of sales tax.

$$\frac{\$52}{\$2.60 \text{ sales tax}} = \frac{\$28}{y \text{ dollars sales tax}}$$

$$\frac{52}{2.6} = \frac{28}{y}$$

$$52 \cdot y = 28 \cdot 2.6$$

$$52y = 72.8$$

$$52y \div 52 = 72.8 \div 52$$

$$y = 1.4$$

His friend will pay $1.40 sales tax.

16. a) When $P = \$50,000$, $r = 0.03$ and $I = Prt$,

$I = 50,000 \cdot 0.03 \cdot t$

$I = 1,500t$

b) When $I = 1,500t$ and $t = 2$,

$I = 1,500 \cdot 2$

$I = 3,000$

The company will earn $3,000 interest in 2 years.

17. Let y be Janet's total sales.

$$\frac{4.5\%}{\$130.50} = \frac{100\%}{y \text{ dollars}}$$

$$\frac{4.5}{130.50} = \frac{100}{y}$$

$$4.5 \cdot y = 130.50 \cdot 100$$

$$4.5y = 13,050$$

$$4.5y \div 4.5 = 13,050 \div 4.5$$

$$y = 2,900$$

Her total sales last week was $2,900.

18. Let y be the amount of vinegar.

$$\frac{y \text{ oz of vinegar}}{35 \text{ oz of salt solution}} = \frac{3 \text{ oz of vinegar}}{7 \text{ oz of salt solution}}$$

$$\frac{y}{35} = \frac{3}{7}$$

$$35 \cdot \frac{y}{35} = 35 \cdot \frac{3}{7}$$

$$y = 15 \text{ oz}$$

15 ounces of vinegar are needed.

19. a) Let y be the length of time.

$$\frac{60 \text{ packets}}{5 \text{ min}} = \frac{240 \text{ packets}}{y \text{ min}}$$

$$\frac{60}{5} = \frac{240}{y}$$

$$60 \cdot y = 5 \cdot 240$$

$$60y = 1,200$$

$$60y \div 60 = 1,200 \div 60$$

$$y = 20 \text{ min}$$

The machine takes 20 minutes to pack 240 packets of pasta.

b) Let x be the number of packets.

$$\frac{60 \text{ packets}}{5 \text{ min}} = \frac{x \text{ packets}}{60 \text{ min}}$$

$$\frac{60}{5} = \frac{x}{60}$$

$$5 \cdot x = 60 \cdot 60$$

$$5x = 3,600$$

$$5x \div 5 = 3,600 \div 5$$

$$x = 720$$

720 packets of pasta can be packed in an hour.

20. Let C be the cost for a 3,600-square foot vacant lot.

$$\frac{C \text{ dollars}}{3,600 \text{ ft}^2} = \frac{\$129,920}{2,000 \text{ ft}^2}$$

$$\frac{C}{3,600} = \frac{129,920}{2,000}$$

$$3,600 \cdot \frac{C}{3,600} = \frac{129,920}{2,000} \cdot 3,600$$

$$C = 233,856$$

The cost of a 3,600-square foot vacant lot is $233,856.

Lesson 5.4

1. For each pair of x and y:

$xy = 100 \cdot 2 = 200$; $xy = 50 \cdot 4 = 200$;

$xy = 10 \cdot 20 = 200$

Yes, y is inversely proportional to x.

The constant of proportionality is 200.

2. For each pair of x and y:

$xy = 6 \cdot 20 = 120$; $xy = 4 \cdot 40 = 160$;

$xy = 2 \cdot 80 = 160$

No, y is not inversely proportional to x.

3. For each pair of x and y:

$xy = 3 \cdot 10 = 30$; $xy = 6 \cdot 20 = 120$;

$xy = 9 \cdot 30 = 270$

No, y is not inversely proportional to x.

4. For each pair of x and y:

$xy = 2 \cdot 210 = 420$; $xy = 6 \cdot 70 = 420$;

$xy = 10 \cdot 42 = 420$

Yes, y is inversely proportional to x.

The constant of proportionality is 420.

5.

$$y = 15x$$

$$y \div x = 15 \div x$$

$$\frac{y}{x} = 15$$

No, y is not inversely proportional to x.

6. Yes, y is inversely proportional to x.

The constant of proportionality is $\frac{1}{4}$.

7.
$$20y = \frac{4}{x}$$
$$20y \cdot x = \frac{4}{x} \cdot x$$
$$20xy = 4$$
$$20xy \div 20 = 4 \div 20$$
$$xy = \frac{1}{5}$$

Yes, y is inversely proportional to x.
The constant of proportionality is $\frac{1}{5}$.

8.
$$xy + 3 = 7$$
$$xy + 3 - 3 = 7 - 3$$
$$xy = 4$$

Yes, y is inversely proportional to x.
The constant of proportionality is 4.

9. Constant of proportionality: $xy = 1 \cdot 10 = 10$

10. Constant of proportionality: $xy = 3 \cdot 5 = 15$

11. Constant of proportionality: $xy = 2 \cdot 0.2 = 0.4$

12. Constant of proportionality: $xy = 2 \cdot 4 = 8$

13. Constant of proportionality: $xy = 4 \cdot 50 = 200$

14. Constant of proportionality: $xy = 4 \cdot 40 = 160$

15. a) Constant of proportionality: $st = 12 \cdot 7 = 84$

b) $st = 84$

c) When $t = 5$ and $st = 84$,
$$s \cdot 5 = 84$$
$$5s = 84$$
$$5s \div 5 = 84 \div 5$$
$$s = 16.8$$

16. a) Constant of proportionality: $xy = 7.5 \cdot 6 = 45$

b) $xy = 45$

c) When $x = 2$ and $xy = 45$,
$$2 \cdot y = 45$$
$$2y = 45$$
$$2y \div 2 = 45 \div 2$$
$$y = 22.5$$

17. a) Constant of proportionality: $\rho v = 4 \cdot 3 = 12$;
Inverse proportion equation: $\rho v = 12$

b) It represents the mass of Americium.

c) The density of 3 cubic centimeters of Americium is 4 grams per cubic centimeter.

18. a) Constant of proportionality:
$tr = 2 \cdot 300 = 600$
Inverse proportion equation: $rt = 600$

b) It takes 2 minutes to fill the tank when the water is flowing at a rate of 300 pints per minute.

c) From the graph, it will take 4 minutes.

19. Constant of proportionality: $yx = 60 \cdot 3\frac{1}{2} = 210$;

Inverse proportion equation: $xy = 210$
When $xy = 210$ and $x = 70$,
$$70 \cdot y = 210$$
$$70y = 210$$
$$70y \div 70 = 210 \div 70$$
$$y = 3 \text{ h}$$
It will take Jeffrey 3 hours to travel from Town P to Town Q.

20. Constant of proportionality: $xy = 16 \cdot 6 = 96$;
Inverse proportion equation: $xy = 96$
When $y = 4$ and $xy = 96$,
$$x \cdot 4 = 96$$
$$4x = 96$$
$$4x \div 4 = 96 \div 4$$
$$x = 24$$

24 children are needed to put the same jigsaw puzzle together in 4 hours.

Brain@Work

1. a) $t = \dfrac{kn}{p}$

b) When $t = \dfrac{kn}{p}$, $t = 21$, $n = 1{,}500$, and $p = 4$,
$$21 = \frac{1{,}500k}{4}$$
$$21 \cdot 4 = \frac{1{,}500k}{4} \cdot 4$$
$$84 = 1{,}500k$$
$$84 \div 1{,}500 = 1{,}500k \div 1{,}500$$
$$0.056 = k$$

When $t = \dfrac{kn}{p}$, $k = 0.056$, $n = 5{,}000$,
and $p = 6$,
$$t = \frac{5{,}000 \cdot 0.056}{6}$$
$$t = 46\frac{2}{3}\text{ h}$$

It will take 6 people about 47 hours to lay 5,000 tiles.

2. a) $R = \dfrac{k\ell}{A}$

b) Doubling the length of a wire increases the resistance by a factor of two.

c) Doubling the diameter of a wire quadruples the resistance.

Cumulative Practice
for Chapters 3 to 5

1. $5.8m + 2.3n - 4.9m - 1.7n$
$= (5.8m - 4.9m) + (2.3n - 1.7n)$
$= 0.9m + 0.6n$

2. $\dfrac{3}{7}x + \dfrac{5}{8} - \dfrac{3}{14}x + \dfrac{1}{4}$
$= \left(\dfrac{3}{7}x - \dfrac{3}{14}x\right) + \left(\dfrac{5}{8} + \dfrac{1}{4}\right)$
$= \left(\dfrac{6}{14}x - \dfrac{3}{14}x\right) + \left(\dfrac{5}{8} + \dfrac{2}{8}\right)$
$= \dfrac{3}{14}x + \dfrac{7}{8}$

3. $-0.6(x + 3y) - 0.4x$
$= (-0.6)(x) + (-0.6)(3y) - 0.4x$
$= -0.6x - 1.8y - 0.4x$
$= (-0.6x - 0.4x) - 1.8y$
$= -x - 1.8y$

4. $-\dfrac{1}{2}\left(\dfrac{2}{3}x - 4\right)$
$= \left(-\dfrac{1}{2}\right)\left(\dfrac{2}{3}x\right) + \left(-\dfrac{1}{2}\right)(-4)$
$= -\dfrac{1}{3}x + 2$

5. $4\left(\dfrac{1}{5}x - 3y\right) + 7y - \dfrac{1}{3}x$
$= 4\left(\dfrac{1}{5}x\right) + 4(-3y) + 7y - \dfrac{1}{3}x$
$= \dfrac{4}{5}x - 12y + 7y - \dfrac{1}{3}x$
$= \left(\dfrac{4}{5}x - \dfrac{1}{3}x\right) + (-12y + 7y)$
$= \left(\dfrac{12}{15}x - \dfrac{5}{15}x\right) + (-5y)$
$= \dfrac{7}{15}x - 5y$

6. $-6(m + 3n) - 4(2m - n)$
$= (-6)(m) + (-6)(3n) + (-4)(2m) + (-4)(-n)$
$= (-6m) + (-18n) + (-8m) + 4n$
$= (-6m - 8m) + (-18n + 4n)$
$= -14m + (-14n)$
$= -14m - 14n$
$= -14(m + n)$

7. $-9x - 45$
$= (-9)(x) + (-9)(5)$
$= (-9)(x + 5)$
$= -9(x + 5)$

8. $18 - 30w + 6k$
$= 6(3) + 6(-5w) + 6(k)$
$= 6(3 - 5w + k)$

9. $45\% \cdot \left(\dfrac{2}{15}\right)\left[(x + 1) \cdot \dfrac{1}{12}y\right]$
$= \dfrac{45}{100} \cdot \left(\dfrac{2}{15}\right)\left[\dfrac{y(x + 1)}{12}\right]$
$= \dfrac{3}{50}\left[\dfrac{y(x + 1)}{12}\right]$
$= \dfrac{y(x + 1)}{200}$
$= \dfrac{xy + y}{200}$

10. $\dfrac{10}{9} \cdot [3x + 12y + (-6z)]$
$= \dfrac{10}{9} \cdot [3(x) + 3(4y) + 3(-2z)]$
$= \dfrac{10}{9} \cdot 3 \cdot (x + 4y - 2z)$
$= \dfrac{10}{3}(x + 4y - 2z)$

11. $5x + 1 = 11$ and $2x = 4$
$2x = 4$
$2x \div 2 = 4 \div 2$
$x = 2$
Then check to see if 2 is the solution of the equation $5x + 1 = 11$.
If $x = 2$, $5x + 1 = 5(2) + 1$
$= 11$
Because the equations have same solution, they are equivalent equations.

12. $\dfrac{1}{3}y = 1$ and $y + 1 = 2$

$\dfrac{1}{3}y = 1$

$3 \cdot \dfrac{1}{3}y = 3 \cdot 1$

$y = 3$
Then check to see if 3 is the solution of the equation $y + 1 = 2$.
If $y = 3$, $y + 1 = 3 + 1$
$= 4 \; (\neq 2)$
Because the equations have different solutions, they are not equivalent equations.

13.
$$10.4 + 2.5y = 15.4$$
$$10.4 + 2.5y - 10.4 = 15.4 - 10.4$$
$$2.5y = 5$$
$$2.5y \div 2.5 = 5 \div 2.5$$
$$y = 2$$

14.
$$1.8(5 - 2y) = 0.9y$$
$$1.8(5) + 1.8(-2y) = 0.9y$$
$$9 - 3.6y = 0.9y$$
$$9 - 3.6y + 3.6y = 0.9y + 3.6y$$
$$9 = 4.5y$$
$$9 \div 4.5 = 4.5y \div 4.5$$
$$2 = y$$

15.
$$2(3p - 4) - 3(5 - 2p) + 18 = 19$$
$$2(3p) + 2(-4) + (-3)(5) + (-3)(-2p) + 18 = 19$$
$$6p - 8 - 15 + 6p + 18 = 19$$
$$12p - 5 = 19$$
$$12p - 5 + 5 = 19 + 5$$
$$12p = 24$$
$$12p \div 12 = 24 \div 12$$
$$p = 2$$

16.
$$9.6 - 2(4.5y + 3) = 1.2(2y - 3) + 3y$$
$$9.6 + (-2)(4.5y) + (-2)(3) = 1.2(2y) + (1.2)$$
$$(-3) + 3y$$
$$9.6 - 9y - 6 = 2.4y - 3.6 + 3y$$
$$3.6 - 9y = 5.4y - 3.6$$
$$3.6 - 9y + 9y = 5.4y - 3.6 + 9y$$
$$3.6 = 14.4y - 3.6$$
$$3.6 + 3.6 = 14.4y - 3.6 + 3.6$$
$$7.2 = 14.4y$$
$$7.2 \div 14.4 = 14.4y \div 14.4$$
$$0.5 = y$$

17.
$$2 - 2(x - 3) > x - 7$$
$$2 + (-2)(x) + (-2)(-3) > x - 7$$
$$2 - 2x + 6 > x - 7$$
$$8 - 2x > x - 7$$
$$8 - 2x + 2x > x - 7 + 2x$$
$$8 > 3x - 7$$
$$8 + 7 > 3x - 7 + 7$$
$$15 > 3x$$
$$15 \div 3 > 3x \div 3$$
$$5 > x$$

18.
$$m - \frac{1}{6}m - 1 \le \frac{1}{3}m + 1$$
$$\frac{5}{6}m - 1 \le \frac{1}{3}m + 1$$
$$\frac{5}{6}m - 1 - \frac{1}{3}m \le \frac{1}{3}m + 1 - \frac{1}{3}m$$
$$\frac{5}{6}m - \frac{2}{6}m - 1 \le 1$$
$$\frac{3}{6}m - 1 \le 1$$
$$\frac{1}{2}m - 1 + 1 \le 1 + 1$$
$$\frac{1}{2}m \le 2$$
$$\frac{1}{2}m \cdot 2 \le 2 \cdot 2$$
$$m \le 4$$

19.
$$11.8 - 0.7b < -9.2$$
$$11.8 - 0.7b + 0.7b < -9.2 + 0.7b$$
$$11.8 < -9.2 + 0.7b$$
$$11.8 + 9.2 < -9.2 + 0.7b + 9.2$$
$$21 < 0.7b$$
$$21 \div 0.7 < 0.7b \div 0.7$$
$$30 < b$$

20.
$$7 - 4(5y - 3) \le 2(3 - y) - 5$$
$$7 + (-4)(5y) + (-4)(-3) \le 2(3) + 2(-y) - 5$$
$$7 - 20y + 12 \le 6 - 2y - 5$$
$$19 - 20y \le 1 - 2y$$
$$19 - 20y + 20y \le 1 - 2y + 20y$$
$$19 \le 1 + 18y$$
$$19 - 1 \le 1 + 18y - 1$$
$$18 \le 18y$$
$$18 \div 18 \le 18y \div 18$$
$$1 \le y$$

21. For each pair of values, x and y:

$$\frac{y}{x} = \frac{3}{0.2} = 15; \quad \frac{y}{x} = \frac{9}{0.6} = 15; \quad \frac{y}{x} = \frac{18}{1.2} = 15$$

So, the table represents a direct proportion. The constant of proportionality is 15.

22. For each pair of values, x and y:
$$x \cdot y = 5 \cdot 45 = 225$$
$$x \cdot y = 15 \cdot 15 = 225$$
$$x \cdot y = 25 \cdot 9 = 225$$
So, the table represents an inverse proportion.
The constant of proportionality is 225.

23. For each pair of values, x and y:
$$\frac{y}{x} = \frac{-160}{20} = -8; \quad \frac{y}{x} = \frac{-320}{40} = -8;$$
$$\frac{y}{x} = \frac{-480}{60} = -8$$

So, the table represents a direct proportion.
The constant of proportionality is -8.

24. $y = \frac{1}{4}x + 5$

The original equation $y = \frac{1}{4}x + 5$ cannot be rewritten as an equivalent equation in the form $y = kx$ or $xy = k$, so it does not represent a direct proportion or an inverse proportion.

25.
$$0.5y = 3.5x$$
$$0.5y \div 0.5 = 3.5x \div 0.5$$
$$y = 7x$$

Because the original equation $0.5y = 3.5x$ can be rewritten as an equivalent equation in the form $y = kx$, it represents a direct proportion.
The constant of proportionality is 7.

26.
$$8y = \frac{72}{x}$$
$$8y \div 8 = \frac{72}{x} \div 8$$
$$y = \frac{9}{x}$$
$$xy = 9$$

Because the original equation $8y = \frac{72}{x}$ can be rewritten as an equivalent equation in the form $xy = k$, it represents an inverse proportion.
The constant of proportionality is 9.

27. Although the graph is a straight line that does not lie along the x- or y-axis, it does not pass through the origin. So, the graph does not represent a direct proportion.
Coordinates (0, 20): $0 \cdot 20 = 0$
The constant of proportionality cannot be 0. So, the graph does not represent an inverse proportion as well.

28. Since the graph is not a straight line, it does not represent a direct proportion.
Coordinates (0, 0): $0 \cdot 0 = 0$
The constant of proportionality cannot be 0. So, the graph does not represent an inverse proportion as well.

29. Coordinates (1, 100) : $1 \cdot 100 = 100$
Coordinates (2, 50) : $2 \cdot 50 = 100$
Coordinates (4, 25) : $4 \cdot 25 = 100$
The graph is a curve and each pair of coordinates x and y gives the product x and y, $x \cdot y$ a nonzero constant. So, the graph represents an inverse proportion.
The constant of proportionality is 100.

30. Constant of proportionality $= \frac{y}{x}$
$$= \frac{70}{10}$$
$$= 7$$
The direct proportion equation is $y = 7x$.
When $x = 5$ and $y = 7x$, $y = 7(5)$
$$= 35$$
When $y = 84$ and $y = 7x$, $84 = 7x$
$$84 \div 7 = 7x \div 7$$
$$12 = x$$

x	5	10	12
y	35	70	84

31. Constant of proportionality $= \frac{y}{x}$
$$= \frac{25}{100}$$
$$= \frac{1}{4}$$
The direct proportion equation is $y = \frac{1}{4}x$.

When $x = 200$ and $y = \frac{1}{4}x$, $y = \frac{1}{4}(200)$
$$= 50$$
When $y = 125$ and $y = \frac{1}{4}x$, $125 = \frac{1}{4}x$
$$4 \cdot 125 = 4 \cdot \frac{1}{4}x$$
$$500 = x$$

x	100	200	500
y	25	50	125

32. Constant of proportionality $= x \cdot y$
$$= 15 \cdot 60$$
$$= 900$$
The inverse proportion equation is $xy = 900$.
When $x = 30$ and $xy = 900$, $30 \cdot y = 900$
$$\frac{1}{30} \cdot 30 \cdot y = \frac{1}{30} \cdot 900$$
$$y = 30$$

When $y = 20$ and $xy = 900$, $x \cdot 20 = 900$

$$x \cdot 20 \cdot \frac{1}{20} = 900 \cdot \frac{1}{20}$$

$$x = 45$$

x	15	30	45
y	60	30	20

33. Constant of proportionality $= x \cdot y$

$$= 2 \cdot 22.5$$

$$= 45$$

The inverse proportion equation is $xy = 45$.

When $x = 1$ and $xy = 45$, $1 \cdot y = 45$

$$y = 45$$

When $x = 3$ and $xy = 45$, $3 \cdot y = 45$

$$\frac{1}{3} \cdot 3 \cdot y = \frac{1}{3} \cdot 45$$

$$y = 15$$

x	1	2	3
y	45	22.5	15

34. a) Constant of proportionality $= \dfrac{y}{x}$

$$= \frac{4.5}{0.5}$$

$$= 9$$

Direct proportion equation: $y = 9x$

b) When $x = 1.2$ and $y = 9x$, $y = 9 \cdot 1.2$

$$= 10.8$$

c) When $y = 7.2$ and $y = 9x$, $7.2 = 9x$

$$7.2 \div 9 = 9x \div 9$$

$$0.8 = x$$

35. a) Constant of proportionality $= PQ$

$$= 960 \cdot \frac{1}{3}$$

$$= 320$$

b) The inverse proportion equation is $PQ = 320$.

c) When $Q = \dfrac{1}{4}$ and $PQ = 320$,

$$p \cdot \left(\frac{1}{4}\right) = 320$$

$$p \cdot \left(\frac{1}{4}\right) \cdot 4 = 320 \cdot 4$$

$$P = 1{,}280$$

d) When $P = 16$ and $PQ = 320$,

$$16 \cdot Q = 320$$

$$\frac{1}{16} \cdot 16 \cdot Q = \frac{1}{16} \cdot 320$$

$$Q = 20$$

36.

Distance Traveled

a) The graph is a straight line through origin, and it does not lie along the x- or y-axis, So, the distance traveled is directly proportional to the gas usage. Because the graph passes through (1, 20),

Constant of proportionality $= \dfrac{20}{1}$

$$= 20$$

The direct proportion equation is $y = 20x$.

b) From the graph, when $y = 100$, $x = 5$. He needs 5 gallons of gas.

c) From the graph, when $x = 2$, $y = 40$. The car can travel 40 miles.

37. a) Total distance $= (3x + 2y) + \left(2x + \dfrac{1}{2}y\right)$

$$= 3x + 2y + 2x + \frac{1}{2}y$$

$$= (3x + 2x) + \left(2y + \frac{1}{2}y\right)$$

$$= \left(5x + \frac{5}{2}y\right) \text{m}$$

The total distance he walked is $\left(5x + \dfrac{5}{2}y\right)$ meters.

b) Total distance $= \left(5x + \dfrac{5}{2}y\right)$ m

Total time taken $= 30$ min $+ 20$ min
$\qquad\qquad\qquad = 50$ min

Average speed $= \dfrac{\text{Total distance}}{\text{Total time taken}}$

$\qquad\qquad = \left(5x + \dfrac{5}{2}y\right) \div 50$

$\qquad\qquad = 5\left(x + \dfrac{y}{2}\right) \cdot \dfrac{1}{50}$

$\qquad\qquad = \dfrac{1}{10}\left(x + \dfrac{y}{2}\right)$

$\qquad\qquad = \left(\dfrac{x}{10} + \dfrac{y}{20}\right)$ m per min

His average walking speed is $\left(\dfrac{x}{10} + \dfrac{y}{20}\right)$ meters per minute.

38. a) Total number of seashells
$= (3x - 5) + (2x + 1) + \left(\dfrac{1}{4}x + 7\right)$
$= \left(3x + 2x + \dfrac{1}{4}x\right) + (-5 + 1 + 7)$
$= \dfrac{21}{4}x + 3$

b) Total number of seashells $= 45$

$\dfrac{21}{4}x + 3 = 45$

$\dfrac{21}{4}x + 3 - 3 = 45 - 3$

$\dfrac{21}{4}x = 42$

$\dfrac{21}{4}x \cdot \dfrac{4}{21} = 42 \cdot \dfrac{4}{21}$

$x = 8$

When $x = 8$, $3x - 5 = 3(8) - 5$
$\qquad\qquad\qquad\quad = 19$
Ken has 19 seashells.

When $x = 8$, $2x + 1 = 2(8) + 1$
$\qquad\qquad\qquad\quad = 17$
Leon has 17 seashells.

When $x = 8$, $\dfrac{1}{4}x + 7 = \dfrac{1}{4}(8) + 7$
$\qquad\qquad\qquad\qquad = 9$
Mark has 9 seashells.

39. Let x be the number of printed T-shirts sold.
$\qquad\qquad$ Profit $\geq \$250$
$\qquad$ Revenue $-$ Cost $\geq \$250$
$\qquad 14x - (80 + 5x) \geq 250$
$\qquad 14x - 80 - 5x \geq 250$
$\qquad 14x - 5x - 80 \geq 250$
$\qquad\quad 9x - 80 \geq 250$
$\qquad 9x - 80 + 80 \geq 250 + 80$
$\qquad\qquad\quad 9x \geq 330$
$\qquad\quad 9x \div 9 \geq 330 \div 9$
$\qquad\qquad\quad x \geq 36\dfrac{2}{3}$

She must sell at least 37 printed T-shirts to make a profit of at least \$250 for a day.

40. The weight, w pounds, is directly proportional to the number of cans, n.

a) A dozen cans weighing 18 pounds means that when $n = 12$, $w = 18$.

$\qquad$ Constant of proportionality $= \dfrac{w}{n}$

$\qquad\qquad\qquad\qquad\qquad = \dfrac{18}{12}$

$\qquad\qquad\qquad\qquad\qquad = \dfrac{3}{2}$

b) The direct proportion equation is $w = \dfrac{3}{2}n$.

c) When $n = 8$ and $w = \dfrac{3}{2}n$, $w = \dfrac{3}{2} \cdot 8$
$\qquad\qquad\qquad\qquad\qquad\qquad = 12$ lb
$\qquad$ 8 cans of milk powder weigh 12 pounds.

41. Given that the ratio of the number of quarters and dimes $= 4 : 5$ and the total of number of coins in the box is $(6q + 18)$,

a) Number of dimes $= \dfrac{5}{9} \cdot (6q + 18)$

$\qquad\qquad\qquad\qquad = \dfrac{5}{9} \cdot 6q + \dfrac{5}{9} \cdot 18$

$\qquad\qquad\qquad\qquad = \dfrac{10}{3}q + 10$

b) Number of quarters

$\qquad = \dfrac{4}{9} \cdot (6q + 18)$

$\qquad = \dfrac{4}{9} \cdot (6q) + \dfrac{4}{9} \cdot (18)$

$\qquad = \dfrac{8}{3}q + 8$

c) Total value of the coins

$$= 0.10\left(\frac{10}{3}q + 10\right) + 0.25\left(\frac{8}{3}q + 8\right)$$

$$= \frac{1}{10}\left(\frac{10}{3}q + 10\right) + \frac{1}{4}\left(\frac{8}{3}q + 8\right)$$

$$= \frac{1}{10} \cdot \frac{10}{3}q + \frac{1}{10} \cdot 10 + \frac{1}{4} \cdot \frac{8}{3}q + \frac{1}{4} \cdot 8$$

$$= \frac{1}{3}q + 1 + \frac{2}{3}q + 2$$

$$= \frac{1}{3}q + \frac{2}{3}q + 1 + 2$$

$$= (q + 3) \text{ dollars}$$

42. The number of 15-cent hairclips is x. Then the number of 20-cent hairclips is $(16 - x)$.

a) Amount spent on hairclips $\leq \$3$

$$0.15x + 0.20(16 - x) \leq 3$$
$$100 \cdot [0.15x + 0.20(16 - x)] \leq 3 \cdot 100$$
$$15x + 20(16 - x) \leq 300$$

The inequality is $15x + 20(16 - x) \leq 300$.

b)
$$15x + 20(16 - x) \leq 300$$
$$15x + 20(16) + 20(-x) \leq 300$$
$$15x + 320 - 20x \leq 300$$
$$-5x + 320 \leq 300$$
$$-5x + 320 - 320 \leq 300 - 320$$
$$-5x \leq -20$$
$$-5x \div (-5) \geq -20 \div (-5)$$
$$x \geq 4$$

She bought at least 4 pieces of 15-cent hairclips.

43. Let the number of carpenters be n.
Let the number of days be d.
d is inversely proportional to n.

Constant of proportionality $= d \cdot n$
$$= 10 \cdot 6$$
$$= 60$$

The inverse proportion equation is $dn = 60$.
When $d = 5$ and $dn = 60$, $5n = 60$
$$5n \div 5 = 60 \div 5$$
$$n = 12$$

2 more carpenters must be hired.

44. The time, y hours, it takes Johnny to drive from Town P to Town Q varies inversely as his average driving speed, x.

a) Use (30, 6) to find the constant of proportionality.
Constant of proportionality $= x \cdot y$
$$= 30 \cdot 6$$
$$= 180$$

It represents the distance between Town P and Town Q.

b) The equation is $xy = 180$.

c) It means that it will take 6 hours to travel from Town P to Town Q if the average speed of the car is 30 miles per hour.

d) If $x = 60$ and $xy = 180$,
$$60 \cdot y = 180$$
$$\frac{1}{60} \cdot 60 \cdot y = \frac{1}{60} \cdot 180$$
$$y = 3 \text{ h}$$

Johnny will take 3 hours to reach Town Q if he travels at 60 miles per hour.

45. Area of triangle ABP

$$= \frac{1}{2} \cdot \text{Area of base} \cdot \text{Height}$$

$$= \frac{1}{2} \cdot (y + y + 1) \cdot 6$$

$$= 3(2y + 1)$$

$$= (6y + 3) \text{ cm}^2$$

Because the area of triangle ABP is at least 27 cm²,

$$6y + 3 \geq 27$$
$$6y + 3 - 3 \geq 27 - 3$$
$$6y \geq 24$$
$$6y \div 6 \geq 24 \div 6$$
$$y \geq 4$$

The least value of y is 4.